WHAT CAUSES EATING DISORDERS – AND WHAT DO THEY CAUSE?

An Essential Introduction for Anyone Who Would Like to Understand Eating Disorders and How to Overcome Them

Dr. Guido K.W. Frank
with
Zoe E. Vlastos and Megan E. Shott

Copyright © 2016 Guido K.W. Frank, MD

ISBN: 978-1-63491-661-5

All rights reserved. No part of this publication may be reproduced, stored in a retrieval system, or transmitted in any form or by any means, electronic, mechanical, recording or otherwise, without the prior written permission of the author.

Published by BookLocker.com, Inc., St. Petersburg, Florida.

Printed on acid-free paper.

The use of general descriptive names, registered names, trademarks, service marks, etc. in this publication does not imply, even in the absence of a specific statement, that such names are exempt from the relevant protective laws and regulations and therefore free for general use.

This book details the authors' personal experiences with and opinions about Eating Disorders. While the advice and information in this book are believed to be true and accurate at the date of publication, neither the authors, nor the publisher can accept any legal responsibility for any errors or omissions that may have been made. There is no warranty made, expressed or implied, with respect to the material contained herein. You understand that this book is not intended as a substitute for consultation with a licensed healthcare practitioner, such as your physician. The use of this book implies your acceptance of this disclaimer.

BookLocker.com, Inc.
2016

First Edition

About the Author

Dr. Guido Frank is a board certified Adult as well as Child and Adolescent Psychiatrist. He is an Associate Professor in Psychiatry and Neuroscience at Children's Hospital and the University of Colorado. After medical school at the Ludwig-Maximilians-University Munich, Germany, Dr. Frank trained in Psychosomatic Medicine at the Roseneck Center for Behavioral Medicine, Prien, Germany. This included training in cognitive and behavioral therapy, dynamic and family therapy, body therapy, hypnotherapy as well as Feldenkrais therapy. He then joined the Center for Overcoming Problem Eating at the Western Psychiatric Institute and Clinic, Pittsburgh, PA, where he trained in neurobiological research in eating disorders. This was followed by Residency in Adult and then Child and Adolescent Psychiatry at the Western Psychiatric Institute and Clinic, and at the University of California San Diego.

Dr. Frank holds grant funding from the National Institutes of Health and from private foundations. He has received multiple awards from organizations such as the American Academy for Child and Adolescent Psychiatry, the American College of Neuropsychopharmacology, Society of Biological Psychiatry as well as the National Institute of Mental Health.

Foremost, Dr. Frank is a compassionate clinician who is most dedicated to improving his patients' quality of life. His goal is to bridge psychotherapy and biological research for a patient centered approach that tailors treatment based on a person's needs, and thus make recovery more tolerable and successful.

Foreword

Dear Reader,

Eating disorders are problems that are difficult to understand and that can cause much suffering to the individual as well as to family, partners and friends who wish to help. Because the reasons and mechanisms why someone might develop an eating disorder are so diverse, it is often difficult to get a good grasp on eating disorders and how to beat this problem. With this book we would like to provide an easy to read yet in depth and informative guide on eating disorders. My original intention was to provide a guide for patients and families who come to me for treatment. However, in talking with our staff it seemed that this information might be helpful to a wider audience, including professionals who start in this field.

My experience is that eating disorders can be overcome. I would like to emphasize their diversity though and that some individuals can overcome their eating disorder without any "professional" help but others do benefit from it. There is not one approach that fits all. Key is to intervene or treat early and with an approach that takes into account a person's individual history as well as psychological and biological factors that may contribute to the illness. The course however is not predictable and not giving up is key for success.

The title is based on my experience that while there are various factors that may contribute that a person develops an eating disorder, engaging in severe food restriction, binge eating or purging behaviors has a severe impact on the brain, which may significantly complicate recovery. The difficulty to understand eating disorder behavior I believe is due to this complex interaction.

I am most grateful to the people who helped make this book possible, and especially to all the patients and families that I had the privilege to work with over the past 20 years. Specifically I would like to acknowledge and thank my co-authors Zoe Vlastos and Megan Shott, as well as Riley Judd, Maria Kalina, Isabelle Kang, Barbara Mahnen, and Riza Pykkonen for their feedback and contributions.

The artwork on the cover page and in the back of the book is by Tera Proper. In the "Trust Picture" she expresses a key problem for many with anorexia nervosa - the need to develop trust. The "Never Give Up Picture" shows a key quality important for professionals, family members or friends who want to help.

Lastly, all proceeds from the book will go to research on eating disorders with the hope that we will be able to improve the available treatments and make recovery less strenuous and more successful.

Guido K.W. Frank, MD

Table of Contents

1. Introduction - The Unusual Problem

'I know seventy-seven pounds is low but I'm not happy now with the way I am. I want to be a lot less.' This is a testimonial from a woman with anorexia nervosa explaining why she cannot eat enough to maintain a normal body weight (1). Other individuals with eating disorders may never have had a good sense of appetite or satiety and cannot stop eating some or all of the time, even if they try to do so. Some children may tell you that they have been feeling uncomfortable in their body since they can remember. One girl who came to me for treatment at the age of 12 years old told me that she started searching the Internet for thin bodies when she was only four years old. For others the eating disorder developed over the course of a few months when just trying to lose a few pounds and be more physically fit.

Eating disorders come in various forms. The presentations of eating disorders range from the severely emaciated individual with anorexia nervosa, to the person with bulimia nervosa who restricts eating but then frequently loses control and eats large amount of food ("binge eat") only to throw those up, to those individuals with binge eating disorder who binge eat without methods to rid themselves of the food eaten. Importantly, there are also many in-between states of disordered eating. For instance a newly identified group has so called purging disorder, that are individuals who may eat normal amounts of food but use self induced

1

vomiting, or laxatives to avoid weight gain or to lose weight. Although many individuals may not fit exactly into an eating disorder category, they may nevertheless suffer greatly from the eating disorder and the often-associated depression and anxiety.

For most, the existence of eating disorders is difficult to understand, because isn't eating the most natural thing of the world? And it is true that eating disorders, at least on first sight, have little rational explanation to them. Later when we describe and discuss brain biology, you will see that from a biological perspective it may become very difficult to reverse course after being caught in a severe eating disorder. Eating disorder behavior at times can be seen as a self-directed attempt to manage stress, feelings and other problems, however, from a perspective of reason there are typically more effective ways to get emotional relieve. Why one person develops an eating disorder while another gets "only" depression or an anxiety disorder is unknown though, although certain temperament or psychological traits may be risk factors for developing eating disorders.

In this guide we will discuss eating disorders in their path from early onset to full development and recovery. We will explore and describe how someone may present with an eating disorder and the distinct paths and reasons that may result in similar presentations of anorexia or bulimia nervosa or another eating disorder. We will explain the concept of the "perfect storm," which we have developed to help understand eating disorders. In short, the perfect storm model takes into account the biological, psychological, and social factors that influence the development and expression of different eating disorder types. We will explore vulnerabilities to develop an eating disorder, as well as possible changes that might occur during the illness and complicate recovery. We will spend time describing what we know about the brain in eating disorders and how we can make sense of eating disorder behaviors from a biological perspective. Often, it takes a combination of interventions to help a child or an adult to overcome an eating disorder. We will review treatment approaches that have shown benefits. In summary, in this book we hope to present a comprehensive view of presentation, underlying mechanism, and treatment approaches of eating disorders in order to further understanding, increase empathy with individuals with eating disorders, and help patients and their families on the path of recovery.

2. Historical Perspective

Anorexia nervosa is a condition that has been described in various forms for centuries. Severe fasting in religious figures such as Catherine of Siena or Mary, Queen of Scotland was suspected to have been forms of anorexia nervosa. The maybe first formal description of anorexia nervosa is from 1689 by the British physician Richard Morton who writes:

"Mr. Duke's daughter in St. Mary Axe, in the eighteenth year of her age, fell into a total suppression of her monthly courses from a multitude of cares and passions of her mind but without any symptom of the green-sickness following upon it. ... I do not remember that I did ever in all my practice see one that was conversant with the living so much wasted with the greatest degree of consumption (like a skeleton only clad with skin). ... A nervous atrophy, or consumption, is a wasting of the body without any remarkable fever, cough, or shortness of breath; but it is attended with a want of appetite, and a bad digestion, upon which there follows a languishing weakness of nature, and a falling away of the flesh every day more and more."

This description from the 17th century suggests that anorexia nervosa-type behavior is not just a product of our modern times and society, but that it may have a long standing history, although probably occurring less frequently than nowadays. Important here is that if this is a phenomenon that originated long before the current media portrayed ideals of thinness then there may be biological underpinnings that could drive this illness.

Another British physician, Sir William Gull coined the term "anorexia nervosa" in 1873, translated from Latin "nervous absence of appetite". This terminology is not really true though, as we now know that many with anorexia nervosa are hungry, but do not allow themselves to eat.

Anorexia nervosa was first formally included in the American Diagnostic and Statistical Manual of Mental Disorders (DSM) in 1952. A milestone in the history of anorexia nervosa is further the work of Hilde Bruch, a German-born American psychoanalyst, who developed a psychodynamic conceptualization of anorexia nervosa bringing the disorder into the public's eye and understanding. Her theory was based on the effects of early life experience and (lack of) effectiveness of parents responding to their child's needs, which could later lead to an adolescent struggling with autonomy and independence. This view has come into question though and has not been supported by empirical evidence. Schizophrenia, a severe mental disorder with delusions and hallucinations, or autism, a disorder with many interpersonal but also speech difficulties, were thought at some point to be due to so called "refrigerator mothers", suggesting a lack of warmth of mothers toward the child. However, it is now well known that there are various biological mechanisms that are related to those disorders and the concept of the "cold mother" or other simplistic environmental or parental reasons have been discarded. If anything, psychiatric disorders are now viewed as complex problems with a host of factors coming together that might lead to such illnesses.

Bulimia nervosa type behaviors have also been described throughout history. In ancient Rome there was a known practice of binge eating and subsequent self-induced vomiting to relieve oneself in order to eat again during feasts that would often last days. In 1979, and thus not very long ago, Gerald Russell first described bulimia nervosa. He saw it as "an ominous variant of anorexia nervosa," but this view did not hold up and bulimia nervosa is now seen as its own disorder. In 1980 bulimia nervosa was formally recognized as a psychiatric disorder.

Most recently in 2013 binge eating disorder was introduced in the latest version of the DSM. In that edition of this diagnostic manual there were also other new developments in the pursuit of judiciously describing the various forms of eating disorders. The new categories OSFED and UFED were created. Those acronyms stand for "other specified eating and feeding disorders" and "unspecified eating and feeding disorders" respectively and aim to incorporate individuals who did not fit neatly in a diagnostic category before. This is important for those types of eating disorders to be recognized as serious illnesses in order for individuals to be able to receive treatment.

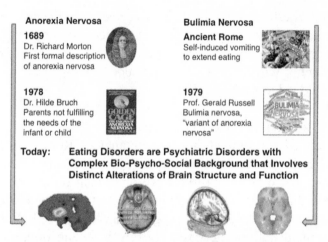

Figure 2.1. Eating disorder behaviors have been in existence for centuries. In the recent past research has shown that there are distinct changes in brain structure and function associated with eating disorders.

Taken together, eating disorders have existed throughout history, but have only recently been formally described and diagnosed. It seems that eating disorders have increased since the 1950s in the western world. Increased awareness could, of course, contribute to this phenomenon. The reasons for such an increase in the diagnosis of eating disorders is not certain, however lifestyle, societal eating habits and what type of food we eat may play important roles. We will explore those aspects later in the book.

3. How To Make The Diagnosis

Over the past 20 years the various forms of eating disorders have been increasingly researched and various sub-types have been identified. There are two major classification systems for mental disorders, the Diagnostic and Statistical Manual for Mental Disorders (DSM), which was developed by the American Psychiatric Association, and the International Statistical Classification of Diseases and Related Health Problems (ICD), which is developed and maintained by the World Health Organization. Here we will use the diagnostic criteria provided by the DSM.

Anorexia Nervosa

Individuals with anorexia nervosa (AN) are typically below 85% expected body weight for age and height but feel fat despite being underweight. However, in the new edition of the Diagnostic and Statistical Manual for Mental Disorders 5 (DSM-5) this strict weight criterion has been dropped, as was the previous diagnostic criterion of loss of regular menses. Two main types of anorexia nervosa have been described. Restricting type anorexia, marked by food restriction and commonly over-exercising, has been distinguished from binge-eating/purging type anorexia, where afflicted individuals eat large amounts of food in a relatively short period of time ("binge eating"), or engage in behaviors to counteract weight gain, such as self-induced vomiting or use of laxatives or diuretics ("purging").

□
Anorexia Nervosa DSM-5 Diagnostic Criteria

1. Persistent restriction of energy intake leading to significantly low body weight (in context of what is minimally expected for age, sex, developmental trajectory, and physical health).

2. Either an intense fear of gaining weight or of becoming fat, or persistent behavior that interferes with weight gain (even though significantly low weight).

3. Disturbance in the way one's body weight or shape is experienced, undue influence of body shape and weight on self-evaluation, or persistent lack of recognition of the seriousness of the current low body weight.

Bulimia Nervosa

Individuals with bulimia nervosa are usually at a normal weight and engage in recurrent binge eating and purging behavior at least once a week for at least three months. Importantly, compensatory behaviors to avoid weight gain may be solely fasting or excessive exercise.

There is often a transition between disorders and stages of illness that can be observed; some individuals develop bulimic behaviors after experiencing anorexia nervosa (about 35%) while others move in the opposite direction, from bulimia nervosa to anorexia like symptoms (about 25-30%).

Bulimia Nervosa DSM-5 Diagnostic Criteria

1. Recurrent episodes of binge eating. An episode of binge eating is characterized by both of the following:

- Eating, in a discrete period of time (e.g. within any 2-hour period), an amount of food that is definitely larger than most people would eat during a similar period of time and under similar circumstances.

- A sense of lack of control over eating during the episode (e.g. a feeling that one cannot stop eating or control what or how much one is eating).

2. Recurrent inappropriate compensatory behavior in order to prevent weight gain, such as self-induced vomiting, misuse of laxatives, diuretics, or other medications, fasting, or excessive exercise.

3. The binge eating and inappropriate compensatory behaviors both occur, on average, at least once a week for three months.

4. Self-evaluation is unduly influenced by body shape and weight.

The disturbance does not occur exclusively during episodes of Anorexia Nervosa.

Binge Eating Disorder

A new diagnosis, "binge eating disorder" (BED), has been introduced in the DSM-5 and involves episodes of excessive eating as in bulimia nervosa but without compensatory behaviors, such as over-exercise or purging.

Binge Eating Disorder DSM-5 Diagnostic Criteria

1. Recurrent episodes of binge eating. An episode of binge eating is characterized by both of the following:

- Eating, in a discrete period of time (e.g. within any 2-hour period), an amount of food that is definitely larger than most people would eat during a similar period of time and under similar circumstances.

- A sense of lack of control over eating during the episode (e.g. a feeling that one cannot stop eating or control what or how much one is eating).

2. The binge eating episodes are associated with three or more of the following:

- Eating much more rapidly than normal, eating until feeling uncomfortably full

- Eating large amounts of food when not feeling physically hungry

-Eating alone because of feeling embarrassed by how much one is eating

- Feeling disgusted with oneself, depressed or very guilty afterward

3. Marked distress regarding binge eating is present

4. Binge eating occurs, on average, at least once a week for three months

5. Binge eating is not associated with the recurrent use of inappropriate compensatory behaviors as in Bulimia Nervosa and does not occur exclusively during the course of Bulimia Nervosa, or Anorexia Nervosa..

Other Specified Feeding or Eating Disorder (OSFED)

Eating disorders that fall into the OSFED category

include *purging disorder*, where individuals engage in regular purge episodes without binge eating, and *atypical anorexia* or *atypical bulimia nervosa*, which

□ **Other Specified Feeding or Eating Disorder (OSFED)**

According to be diagnosed as having OSFED a person must present with feeding or eating behaviors that cause clinically significant distress and impairment in areas of functioning, but do not meet the full criteria for any of the other feeding and eating disorders.

A diagnosis might then be allocated that specifies a specific reason why the presentation does not meet the specifics of another disorder (e.g. Bulimia Nervosa- low frequency). The following are further examples for OSFED:

1. Atypical Anorexia Nervosa: All criteria are met, except weight, despite significant weight loss, the individual's weight is within or above the normal range.

2. Binge Eating Disorder (of low frequency and/or limited duration): All of the criteria for BED are met, except at a lower frequency and/or for less than three months.

3. Bulimia Nervosa (of low frequency and/or limited duration): All of the criteria for Bulimia Nervosa are met, except that the binge eating and inappropriate compensatory behavior occurs at a lower frequency and/or for less than three months.

4. Purging Disorder: Recurrent purging behavior to influence weight or shape in the absence of binge eating

5. Night Eating Syndrome: Recurrent episodes of night eating. Eating after awakening from sleep, or by excessive food consumption after the evening meal. The behavior is not better explained by environmental influences or social norms. The behavior causes significant distress or impairment. The behavior is not better explained by another mental health disorder (e.q. BED).

recognize syndromes that are shy of a diagnostic criterion for the full disorder but nevertheless warrant recognition and treatment.

This is an important new category. One could argue that those individuals have "only a mild form" of an eating disorder. However, this is not correct. Mortality rate (number of deaths) in this group is elevated as in other eating disorder groups, including rate of suicide.

Avoidant/Restrictive Food Intake Disorder (ARFID)

This is a condition typically first seen early on in life where children do not thrive well, avoid food and feel "uncomfortable" eating. It is often associated with fear and pain when eating, but without the typical fear of weight gain as in anorexia nervosa. Those patients sometimes go through years of medical exams and work ups but no specific cause can be found.

Patients with ARFID or others with for instance pain conditions around eating may eventually be referred to eating disorders treatment programs after sometimes years of medical referrals and examinations. This can feel unsatisfactory to both the patient and the family as those patients "do not fit in" the typical program. Primary symptoms such as nausea or pain seem to require a medical explanation, but the truth is that often there is no physical correlate or specific problem in the intestines that can be discovered. In those cases the family then may feel "stuck" with behavioral health providers who may focus on managing stress, eating despite the

□

Avoidant/Restrictive Food Intake Disorder (ARFID)

To be diagnosed as having ARFID a person must display

1. An Eating or Feeding disturbance as manifested by persistent failure to meet appropriate nutritional and/or energy needs associated with one (or more) of the following:

- Significant loss of weight (or failure to achieve expected weight gain or faltering growth in children).

- Significant nutritional deficiency

- Dependence on enteral feeding or oral nutritional supplements

- Marked interference with psychosocial functioning

2. The behavior is not better explained by lack of available food or by an associated culturally sanctioned practice.

3. The behavior does not occur exclusively during the course of anorexia nervosa or bulimia nervosa, and there is no evidence of a disturbance in the way one's body weight or shape is experienced.

4. The eating disturbance is not attributed to a medical condition, or better explained by another mental health disorder. When it does occur in the presence of another condition/disorder, the behavior exceeds what is usually associated, and warrants additional clinical attention.

discomfort and working on ignoring the condition. In that case it is highly important that the treatment team tailors an individualized (as much as possible) approach for those children, adolescents or adults as an eating disorder program is often still the best place for treatment.

Unspecified Feeding or Eating Disorder (UFED)

This is the category for eating disorders that do not fit any of the other categories, yet the health provider feels that the condition does constitute an eating disorder.

□

Unspecified Feeding or Eating Disorder (UFED)

This category applies to where behaviors cause clinically significant distress/impairment of functioning, but do not meet the full criteria of any of the Feeding or Eating Disorder criteria. This category may be used by clinicians where a clinician chooses not to specify why criteria are not met, including presentations where there may be insufficient information to make a more specific diagnosis (e.g. in emergency room settings).

4. Eating Disorders Are Severe and Dangerous Disorders

Individuals with anorexia and bulimia nervosa (as well as other eating disorders) have approximately 1.6 times the mortality rate of the general population for all causes of death, and 4 to 6.5 times the mortality rate of the general population for suicide (2). The highest mortality in eating disorders is usually between 16 and 29 years of age (3). Furthermore, eating disorders have the highest mortality rate among the psychiatric disorders. Many stereotypes and misconceptions of eating disorders exist, which hinders understanding and treatment. Even professionals sometimes do not recognize that an eating disorder in fact exists because their client "isn't skinny enough" or "doesn't throw up". However, the new DSM-5 now recognizes (much better than previous editions of that manual) that there are many "sub-threshold" forms of eating disorders, and while they may not fit the typical categories, they nevertheless cause tremendous distress and suffering. In this context, it is also very important to recognize that eating disorders are associated with other problems such as depressive and anxiety disorders.

Epidemiologic data show that eating disorders occur more frequently in women than in men, but occurrence in males is higher than previously thought. Hudson et al (2007) (4) found in a US study that about 0.9% of the female and 0.3% of the male population have anorexia nervosa, about 1.5% of the female and

0.5% of the male population have bulimia nervosa and approximately 3.5% of females and 2.0% of males suffer from binge eating disorder. Anxiety disorders co-occur in 48-80% of individuals with an eating disorder, mood disorder such as depression occur in 42-71% of individuals with eating disorders, and alcohol or substance use problems occur in 23-36% of individuals with an eating disorder. One often literally cannot see that a person has an eating disorder, especially because those individuals can be highly productive, very selfless, making sure that everything is perfect, a behavior that is highly rewarded in our society. However, when we look at all the facts, how eating disorder behaviors can interfere with well being, rather than stereotypes and misconceptions, one can see that eating disorders are severe illnesses that merit our attention.

There are many medical consequences that result from food restriction, self-induced vomiting, binge eating, and excessive exercise. The recent Special Issue on Medical Complications in Eating Disorders in the International Journal of Eating Disorders provides a comprehensive overview (5).

Anorexia nervosa has been associated with delayed gastric motility (movement of the stomach), gastric emptying and intestinal transit, across the entire intestine. This may be a consequence of malnourishment, self-induced purging or may also occur during treatment and recovery with nutritional rehabilitation. Fullness and abdominal discomfort are therefore very common or even to be expected during the recovery process. There have changes in mass and function of the heart been found, especially in anorexia nervosa. Frequently, bradycardia (low heart rate), hypotension (low blood pressure) can be seen, which can necessitate a medical admission. Because the blood vessels do not contract well, individuals may get dizzy or pass out when standing up quickly. Sudden death (!) may occur in anorexia nervosa. Some have suggested abnormal rhythms of the heart as a cause but it is not clear whether this is indeed the cause. Self-induced vomiting has been associated with causing damage to the teeth and esophagus from the acidic stomach content. Russell's sign is the presence of lesions or scars on the hands caused by repeated scraping of the back of the hand against the upper teeth during gagging to induce vomiting. This has been described in various case reports, but may be much less common than previously thought. Sometimes the salivary glands, located near the mouth and just before the ear, may be swollen after extensive vomiting.

The use of substances to induce vomiting may be associated with severe damage to the heart, and leading to death. The Ipecac syrup, which was the most frequently used drug for that purpose, has been taken off the market in the US for that reason. Self-induced vomiting as well as the use of laxatives and diuretics can lead to low potassium, sodium and chloride in the blood as well as dehydration, leading to so called "metabolic alkalosis", a condition where the balance between positive and negative ions in the blood gets disturbed. That in turn can lead to damage to heart and kidney function as well as muscle break down, which can be fatal. Purging is therefore a serious, damaging and dangerous behavior that cannot be underestimated.

There are also many obstetric and gynecologic complications found in individuals with eating disorders. Those abnormalities include infertility (inability to get pregnant), unplanned pregnancies, miscarriage, damage to the health of the unborn and infants including small head circumference most likely due to poor nutrition.

Other conditions are also more commonly observed, such as postpartum depression, anxiety, sexual dysfunction and gynecologic cancer complications. Polycystic ovarian syndrome has been associated with bulimia nervosa; obesity and related health problems often result from binge eating disorder.

A common problem in anorexia nervosa is low bone mass density and increasing the risk for fractures. The reason for this is probably a combination of the insufficient food intake and low sex hormone (estrogen, progesterone) levels in the body. Hormone replacement may help, but the data available are not entirely clear. Importantly, the body builds up bone mass and density approximately up to the age of 30 years. Years with anorexia nervosa therefore may be "lost years" for bone build up and one may have less solid bones for the rest of her or his life. Binge eating disorder is typically associated with obesity, high blood fats and increased risk for heart disease and diabetes. Nutritional rehabilitation or "refeeding" in anorexia nervosa can have its own danger, the so-called "refeeding syndrome" with hypophosphatemia (low phosphorous) in the blood, which can be dangerous. However, this syndrome typically occurs, if it does occur, within 3-10 after treatment begin and if low phosphorous does occur this can be easily corrected with substitution as a - typically oral - medication.

The longer one has an eating disorder, the more likely it is that those behaviors become habits that then become increasingly more difficult to get rid of. When an adolescent has an eating disorder it is usually most helpful when the parents or guardians are highly involved in the care and help in the recovery process. The leverage that parents have and need to use cannot be underestimated. When an individual is an adult the eating disorder may be so strong that it becomes exceedingly difficult for a person with an eating disorder to overcome it. This I believe has to do with brain changes that occur with the ongoing eating disorder behavior, as well as psychologically the eating disorder becoming part of the person's identity.

Taken together, it cannot be stressed enough that eating disorders can be detrimental. Obviously, not every attempt to exercise more, be more mindful with eating or wanting to lose weight when overweight is or will become an eating disorder. However, if one is much or most of the time preoccupied with food, weight and shape, if aspects of normal life suffer, if friendships get neglected, if medical complications occur such as very low blood pressure, becoming dizzy or fainting, if exercise and behaviors around food interfere with school or work, etc. it has become a problem that needs immediate attention.

5. How Can This Be?

Why would someone not want to eat, one of the most basic mechanisms of life? Typically when parents or loved ones of a person with an eating disorder are faced with this question, there is – in my opinion right fully so – much consternation and disbelief. This seemingly impenetrable wall of food refusal or the overwhelming urges to binge or purge often seem volitional, which may create anger and a sense of "why don't you just [eat], [stop binge eating], [purging] etc.?" It is difficult to understand why an individual engages in these self-destructive behaviors.

Are eating disorders then a product of "choosing" a certain lifestyle? Could someone "just get over it" if only that person wanted to? This would be a very simple solution to a severe problem and based on experience not very likely or easy to do. Aside from body wasting, distorted thinking about one's body, abnormalities in electrolytes, and other changes in laboratory values, there is also often a true sense of personal emotional pain in individuals with eating disorders. This may be driven by the many internal conflicts whether and what to eat, whether one can go out with friends to have a meal, what to wear because of fear of looking too fat, etc. On the other hand, one may want to consider the comments made by Kate Taylor, a writer for Slate Magazine, who herself has recovered from anorexia nervosa and talks about the willfulness seen in individuals with eating disorders.

She wrote: "The disease [anorexia nervosa] often makes them feel special and unique. Until we discard the victim model and admit that anorexia, though destructive, often fulfills a deep personal need, we can't begin to investigate what makes a person vulnerable to it."

Many individuals, especially early during the course of the eating disorder, deny any "problem" or "suffering". By definition a "disorder" is interfering with normal life and a true eating disorder meeting the threshold criteria interferes with normal life. But the individual often disagrees and does not see any reason to seek treatment or make any changes in behavior especially around eating. The ethical ramifications around treatment, such as hospitalization against someone's will for instance, are difficult to solve and create anger for the patients and a dilemma for the treatment providers. Children and adolescents are brought to treatment by their parents and strong involvement from the parents in the treatment process is invaluable. For adults who have an eating disorder the decision is all to themselves, which is often overwhelming.

For individuals with an eating disorder the disorder behavior may be a survival mechanism when all other options seem impossible to them. While many (especially adults) may understand the dangers and problems of an eating disorder and recognize the "cost" of the disorder, it may still seem to be the lesser evil when compared to the seemingly unsurpassable fears and hurdles of life. Understanding those connections is especially difficult for children below the age of 12 years old. Typically these youngsters have not yet developed a more abstract view of the world and they struggle to apply concepts learned in one situation to another situation, to long-term goals, or to past or future events. Still, those children are caught in the eating disorder thoughts that create an unsolvable problem in their lives.

Thus, one has to imagine the tremendous conflict within a person with an eating disorder. Many individuals with eating disorders describe the feeling of "being in the disorder" as "safe", "predictable" and "comforting," while attempts to recover and the uncertainty of life without the eating disorder are extremely scary and difficult to tolerate. While it may externally appear that the individual with an eating disorder has a "choice" to engage in the disorder or not, internally he or she cannot tolerate life without the disorder and therefore does not have any sense of true control. Once in the process of developing an eating disorder, those individuals' anxious personality traits increasingly get in the way of managing life in a healthy way and the eating disorder is typically seen, felt or experienced as a safe haven, the only place to find peace, relief from stress, or a sense of control. This drive to pursue eating disorder behavior is most difficult to understand. Individuals with depression or anxiety typically do not want to feel that way and have a motivation to not have those feelings. With eating disorders it is more complicated and individuals are usually ambivalent about getting rid of the disorder especially at the beginning of treatment.

6. How Could This Happen?

So who is at fault? This is in fact the first question we should stop asking, as there is no single factor or person that causes an eating disorder. Rather there are a variety of factors that come together, depending on the individual person. When Hilde Bruch first described her concept of anorexia nervosa she put a lot of responsibility on the parents. Her claim that problems with separation and individuation in adolescence may stem from parents not fulfilling the needs of the infant or child earlier in life is problematic in that it does not match reality, at least not for many or even most. The development of an eating disorder is complex and unique to each individual. Bruch's theory is just one of many possible paths of how someone may develop an eating disorder.

We propose here a bio-psycho-social model of illness development that includes many aspects of stress or biological predisposition that are most likely involved together with environmental factors. The bio-psycho-social approach to psychiatric illness is a model developed by George Engel (6) to better understand psychological and psychiatric problems. Over the years researchers have recognized that most psychiatric and psychological disorders such as depression, anxiety and also eating disorders do not have only one cause but rather are made up of a combination of problems ("multifactorial") that come together. One important aspect of these disorders is that most have a genetic background, meaning that they run in families. Researchers have also found various changes in brain structure and function in these disorders (which we will discuss in more detail in a later chapter) and that these alterations could drive problem or illness behavior. These are part of the biological model. The psychological part of the model refers to an individual's thoughts, emotions and behaviors that could be dysfunctional and drive unhealthy behavior. For instance a person may think of herself (or himself) as worthless; low mood and anxiety prevent her or him from trying to and then actually achieve, which further supports the self-perception of worthlessness, and this becomes a vicious and self-reinforcing cycle. Lastly, the social part of the model takes into account economical, environmental, and cultural factors that could all contribute to the problem. In fact, eating disorders are more common in the so-called developed western world, and media influences have been associated with eating disorders.

To summarize, there are signs and symptoms that individuals with eating or other disorders share, but by the same time everybody has a personal history, has a very personal path into the disorder that includes a varying degree of biological, psychological and social factors. Thus treatment will include parts that are important for each individual (such as nutritional rehabilitation in anorexia nervosa, stopping binge eating and purging in bulimia nervosa, etc.), but each individual should also have a personalized path out of it, receive intervention(s) in support of the individual recovery.

Important in this combination of factors are biologically determined traits that are common in many patients with eating disorders. Most individuals with eating disorders share anxious traits; they often have a disposition to worry, feel uncomfortable with uncertainty, and feel uneasy when things happen unexpectedly. These traits often go hand in hand with perfectionism and high achievement, which are behaviors that we value in our society. I have often seen children who never had a good sense of self or good self-esteem and instead experience a very deep-sitting emptiness. I have often wondered whether this is a form of depression. This is an especially interesting question as depression commonly goes along with eating disorders, whether independent from the eating disorder or emerging during its course. However, I believe that this emptiness may reflect a deeper problem that may have to do with how the child feels attached to the world and the people in her or his environment. This could be part of the psychological part contributing to eating disorder development. One could argue that this is indeed where the parents' fault lies along the lines of Hilde Bruch's theory. However, I cannot agree with this mindset. I think it is much more complex and one should not jump to fast conclusions. I rather believe that high trait anxiety may interfere with feeling a sense of safety in this world from early on and harm avoidance and perfectionism may be means to manage this lack of sense of safety. When then hurdles occur that are difficult to master (social environment influences), the eating disorder may provide a new, yet fragile and rather perceived than true, sense of safety. In the next chapter we will discuss personality traits and their effects in more detail.

Here are now real life examples, stories of youth and adults that I have worked with, how their eating disorder developed and what patterns I have seen across many individuals.

Real life examples

On one end of the spectrum there is the child or adolescent who never had a particular problem, but attended health class where she got the message that one should watch what one eats. For instance, she may have gotten the message not only to refrain from eating "junk food" but also be careful about eating too much sugar and fat. This child may then be a bit anxious about deleterious health effects and start to reduce snacks and exercise a bit more. After a while these actions may not seem to be enough and she may stop eating desserts and gradually cut out more and more foods that seem unhealthy. This child may then start to watch her body weight and after just a few months she may be in a cycle that she cannot escape; she may be too afraid to go back to normal eating, food makes her very guilty, and then she is on a path of continuous weight loss. This behavior is often hidden from parents and it may take quite a while before the disorder is discovered. Frequently the low body weight and low heart rate come up during the annual well visit at the pediatrician's office. It seems that in these cases there is a very strong biological component where food restriction quickly alters brain mechanisms that are very difficult to control and revert.

Another possible pathway of development occurs in a child or teenager who is very achievement oriented. This child is the type who gets all "As," the parents report that there was never a problem motivating the child, and she or he even may have been a big helper in the family with other siblings, etc. For children who are bright and hard working, elementary school is usually easy to master and everything feels perfect and well controlled. However, in middle school life gets much harder with increased academic demand and an often difficult social transition. Friendships from the past five years may be difficult to maintain. All of these changes bring chaos into a previously well-controlled world. There may be also a set back in sports and the youngster does not get on a certain team or does not perform as well as she/he wanted. This often triggers the drive to exercise more in order to be better and the idea that losing some weight might also help with athletic performance may push the child to restrict food. Some may just lose weight while others struggle with the food restriction and have to start binge eating at some point, as they cannot tolerate the food deprivation. These kids often have a big problem aside from the eating disorder itself; they have to learn to handle the sense of imperfection and maybe being just like other kids in various ways. The conflict here is that the eating disorder can give them the experience of being able to be "perfect in something" and this feeling is often strong enough to continue the behavior. Any attempts from parents or treatment providers to help treat the eating disorder are then only seen as interference in this quest for perfection and self-perceived happiness.

Many children with eating disorders, especially anorexia nervosa, tend to be very compliant, socially adapted, and trying to please (at least on the outside), but a substantial subset, maybe up to 30 percent, may display significant oppositional defiant behaviors in the context of the eating disorder. They may become verbally or even physically assaultive and emotionally very easily deregulated. This behavior is often reminiscent of a toddler who is in the process of learning to regulate strong emotions. For adolescents with eating disorders this may be the first time in their life that they face a hurdle that is not easy to overcome. In addition, treatment is typically geared to give the parents control of meal preparation and take back other control. This normal family hierarchy where the parents are in charge is difficult for the child to tolerate and stimulates oppositional behaviors. It often seems that there is then a reversal of the normal hierarchy and the parents become afraid of the reaction of the child. However, not to take back control would be a form of enabling the eating disorder. I have seen for instance the youngster who tells the parent that she could only eat from a certain (very expensive) healthy food store and the parents would buy every day for maybe $50 very small amounts of food, worth a few hundred calories, and that would be all that the child would eat. However, the parent is afraid of upsetting the child even more, and may go along with the child's wishes because the child would eat "at least something". However that is behavior that enables the eating disorder. Even if kids have tantrums, "scream and yell", one cannot support food restriction binge eating or purging, or excessive exercise. Some youngsters when they are faced with an intensive treatment program have severe behavior outbursts and may even need medication to help them manage the situation, but they have to submit to learn normal eating with the parent's support and supervision, and without that recovery will not happen. I like to tell in that context parents that they need to be a "warm and empathic drill sergeant", that is be steadfast in the supervision of eating, making sure the child takes in what is needed, yet in an empathic attitude, understanding how hard this is for the child.

When adults present for treatment then that is usually voluntary but nevertheless there is very often a very high degree of ambivalence toward eating normal amounts of food and gaining weight for instance. This leads at times to power struggles between therapist and patient. It often takes an extraordinary amount of energy to avoid such struggles and on the other hand work with the patient in a way that the patient can "buy into" and help her or his motivation to change behaviors. The art here is to make the difficult process of recovery not the goal of the therapist, but that of the patient. This seems so obvious, but the ambivalence toward "letting go of the eating disorder" makes this process very difficult. My approach to that in general is to use cognitive strategies to help the patient see how much the eating disorder is rather destructive as opposed to be a helpful friend. In fact I like to compare the eating disorder to an abusive spouse. Although one wishes that the relationship works out and likes to see the good, the truth is that there is abuse that cannot and should not be tolerated. The next step in therapy then is to offer ways to replace the eating disorder, provide a new outlook on life, with means to reduce stress, help with self-esteem and help create a sense of self and safety, in order to life a better, more fulfilling life. However, change is difficult and often frightening, and this has to be acknowledged and addressed over and over again.

Another group of children may have been "chubby," overweight, or obese either from a young age or may have developed high weight later in childhood. This could be due to a genetic disposition, or stress eating (depression may contribute), or from family habits of everyone eating more than what the body needs. Usually these children learn early on from their classmates that they weigh more than others their age and may get teased. This typically nags on the individual's self esteem and may predispose them to low mood and depressive feelings. When other problems arise, for instance stress at school or within the family, they feel more down and at this point they may come up with the idea that they should make an effort to lower their body weight in order to feel happier and be more liked. After changing eating habits and possibly exercising more, they lose weight and receive positive feedback from the environment. This feedback promotes more weight loss. However, the new behavior is difficult to maintain for many, the weight loss does not occur steadily, and losing weight may hit a plateau, which is experienced as very frightening and could lead to extremes of food restriction or exercising. A problem that then often arises is that even when a normal weight is achieved, the individual may not be able to stop excessive food restriction and exercise.

Many individuals with eating disorders put themselves on a very strict diet. For example consuming only 200 calories per day or restricting meals to a piece of fruit for breakfast, half a cup of rice without anything added for lunch, and more fruits or vegetables for dinner. Others may have days where they fast entirely. Low food intake is hard to maintain though and some individuals cannot resist intermittently eating large amounts of food, which then creates severe feelings of guilt. While food restriction is the typical behavior in anorexia nervosa, food is also commonly restricted in bulimia nervosa. In which case it often happens during the day and is followed by nightly binges and subsequent purging behaviors when the individual is alone.

Some individuals report that they never felt comfortable in their body. While for some the cause of that feeling is uncertain, for others a history of sexual abuse may explain feeling uncomfortable in their own body. Sexual abuse is not only a risk factor for eating disorders but also for other psychiatric illnesses though. It is frequently reported that feelings of being uncomfortable in one's body manifests as feeling fat or seeing one's self as fat. However, this is typically tied to a fear of a specific body weight and it is unclear yet what drives the anxiety, whether it is indeed a misperception or more driven by fear of being at a certain weight. The concept of mind-body-fusion was developed in the past, which provides a possible concept for those dynamics: Eating is in the person's mind associated with weight gain and this in turn makes a person feel fat. Eating then automatically triggers feeling fat. That seems to me a logical course of events that drives body image distortion and feeling fat, while even being underweight.

Thus far we have mostly discussed restricting or the combination of restricting with binge eating. However, on the other end of the spectrum are individuals who are not able to control the amount they eat. They either snack much of the day or have distinct binge eating episodes. This behavior is typically associated with increasing weight gain and obesity. They often learn that food reduces stress or anxiety or improves mood – at least for a short time –, which further reinforces eating when stressed or anxious. In fact basic research has shown that carbohydrates reduce anxiety-transmitting chemicals in the brain, such as the neurotransmitter noradrenaline. These individuals struggle with their thoughts and feelings very similarly to individuals with anorexia and bulimia nervosa despite looking different and having a high body weight. The important part here is that their eating disorder is as severe as other eating disorders such as anorexia nervosa. These individuals are often very anxious, depressed, and often suicidal. A problem that has for the longest time not been well recognized up to just recently is binge eating disorder. Individuals with binge eating disorder are often seen as simply eating too much and not having enough will power to manage overeating better. However, that attitude is not justified well in the least. There is obviously a problem with not being able to control eating, which is associated with a very high amount of suffering as well as frequently anxiety and depression. It also seems that these individuals are stuck in a routine for which there is no exit strategy that seems to work. What I also often have seen is that individuals with binge eating disorder who are high in body weight might appear as strong and having a "thick skin". Very much the opposite is often the case. In reality those individuals are rather sensitive and their emotions may not be stable at all. I think it is most important that we recognize that – similar to addition disorders – it is very difficult to get out of those behaviors and it takes a lot of work often to be able to stop the binge eating.

As pointed out, eating disorders most commonly develop during adolescence, but in some these problems start somewhat later, such as in college. These individuals have often struggled with anxiety or depression in younger years already. The behaviors are typically very similar to youth with respect to food restriction, over exercising, and binge / purge behaviors being prominent. However, adults are typically more cognitively insightful, although one has to be careful to distinguish between cognitive insight and emotional insight. Cognitive insight can be seen as an understanding of a problem but not being able to really embrace this knowledge and make behavior changes. When a person has true emotional insight then, even if the knowledge and understanding are hard to accept, the person is willing to do so and is at a point where she is actively making behavior changes for the better.

There are a significant number of individuals who live for decades with an eating disorder and may keep it a secret. I once worked with a woman who was married and had a very clear schedule when she would allow herself to binge or purge to keep these activities entirely secret from her husband. The couple had a routine where he went to the gym every Saturday morning and that was her fixed time during the week when she could fit the eating disorder in without anyone ever learning about it. She also had some more flexible opportunities during the week, but that Saturday time was something she was looking forward to or maybe feeling she needed all throughout the week. She eventually came to treatment when she realized that this preoccupation was taking away from her life, although on the outside she was functioning well. The take home point here is that eating disorder behavior may be entirely shielded from and a secret to the environment.

Some are severely underweight, it is obvious that they are extremely thin or malnourished, but these individuals can be highly productive in any type of profession, maintain high activity levels, are involved with or without children, and seem happy and cheerful. However, this is often to a great degree driven by the need to be always active and not have to sit still because in moments of stillness one may be confronted with one's self or one's body along with the traits of perfectionism and fears of failure. Our society values perfectionism highly, but unrestrained perfectionism and an inability to take breaks or accept certain limitations may come at a great cost. At some point the eating disorder does take away strength and ability to function well and then the individual may be in a truly desperate place. Often the only way to get better is to eventually let go of what is perceived as the person's best friend and companion, the eating disorder.

An important aspect of all these and other brain health conditions is that they affect not only the specific person, but also a whole system. A mother or father struggling with a problem affects children, relatives, and sometimes neighbors. Similarly, when children struggle their behavior has huge impact on their parents

and recovery means that a whole family system will be
healthier.

7. Personality, Temperament and Character, and Comorbidity

Personality has been defined in various ways. One such definition comes from C. Robert Cloninger (1994). He described temperament as "automatic responses to emotional stimuli that determine habits and moods, and character as "self-aware concepts that influence our voluntary intentions and attitudes". Temperament is thought to be heritable, so called "traits" that are stable throughout life, and do not change much. For instance, a person who is genetically predisposed to be anxious may be anxious though his/her entire life. Character on the other hand is thought to be a product of the interaction between temperament and the environment a person has been living in, thus, character should evolve throughout life.

The predisposition to be anxious, to worry about lots of things is typically elevated in individuals with eating disorders. A variety of research studies have indicated that anxiety disorders often occur long before the development of an eating disorder. Generalized anxiety disorder (GAD) is especially frequent. Individuals with GAD tend to worry about every day life issues such as getting bad grades at school, family members may have an accident, losing friends, getting into a tornado, etc. The truth is that any of those things could happen, luckily the likelihood is typically rather small, yet the small chance gets overemphasized (although some do live in truly dangerous circumstances, which has to be distinguished from exaggerated anxiety).

Other anxiety disorders co-occur with eating disorders including social anxiety disorder, which is characterized by individuals feeing fearful of scrutiny from others in their environments and are afraid of embarrassing themselves.

Underlying those behaviors are anxious traits that drive the outward anxiety. Behavioral traits are genetically determined predispositions to behavior. The field of Psychology has researched behavioral traits and several questionnaires have been developed. For instance Cloninger has developed the temperament and character inventory. Traits that have frequently been found to be different in individuals with anorexia nervosa include high harm avoidance, low novelty seeking, and low reward dependence. Bulimia nervosa has been associated with high harm avoidance and high novelty seeking. Harm avoidance is a trait that motivates an individual to "stay out of trouble" or to not engage in anything that might lead to mistakes. Novelty seeking is a trait that drives a person to avoid punishment. These individuals may get into trouble but then "run away from it to avert repercussions." In anorexia nervosa the combination of high harm avoidance, low novelty seeking, and low reward dependence may support the frequently seen withdrawal behaviors and seemingly being not interested in much social contact. In bulimia nervosa the combination of high harm avoidance and high novelty seeking may create an internal conflict and tension as those traits are opposed to each other. One could argue that they may reflect the variation between times of food restriction with intermittent times of binge eating and purging.

Another trait behavior that has been researched is intolerance of uncertainty (IUS), which is elevated in anorexia and bulimia nervosa and may drive harm avoidance. This would be a very credible mechanism. If an individual cannot tolerate uncertainty well, then they may stay out of situations that could create problems, which may be reflected in high harm avoidance.

Another construct is Sensitivity to Reward and Punishment from the Sensitivity to Reward and Punishment Questionnaire (SPSRQ). This assessment tests internal responsiveness to positive and negative stimuli. In anorexia nervosa and bulimia nervosa both sensitivity to reward and sensitivity to punishment are elevated when ill. However, after recovery it seems that only sensitivity to punishment is elevated compared to healthy individuals. This suggests that there are biological mechanisms that drive those behaviors that are exaggerated when actively ill but at least in part normalize when recovered. It is often hard to understand how sensitive individuals with eating disorder are to stimuli from the environment, especially in anorexia nervosa. I have a lot of empathy for individuals with eating disorders and how unpleasant it must feel when one is so sensitive. It is easy for the outside world to try to reassure an individual who is struggling, with comments such as "things will be fine" or " just get through or over it." However, if you are very easily torn and feel pushed around by environmental stimuli your life is miserable, as you constantly have to live in fear that something unexpected might happen that could have a large emotional impact on you.

Another very commonly seen trait seen in eating disorders is perfectionism, as pointed out earlier. Individuals who are very perfectionistic often redo work because they are not satisfied with the product, which can cause problems when the person does not finish her or his work, or neglect social situations because of the need to "fix things" until it "feels right", etc. Perfectionism is a highly valued and praised trait in our perfectionism-preoccupied world. This may help a kid get straight As in school but leads to trouble if the "wrong" behavior becomes perfected, as in the case of an eating disorder. Some need to do things perfectly in order to have the feeling to be the best, others are highly afraid of failure and feeling worthless, which drives the perfectionism. Many parents talk about a "perfect child" that never caused trouble or problems until the eating disorder.

A problem with perfectionism is that children may cruise through childhood and early adolescence and the parents may never have had to discipline their child, the child never struggled with getting homework done, etc. Unfortunately, this may prevent many from learning normal emotion regulation, because there was never a reason for friction. Then when the eating disorder develops this creates for some the first severe conflict. Adolescents then often act like toddlers, throwing tantrums when their parents try to provide structure around meal planning. Perfectionism and how to deal with it are often major parts of psychotherapy.

In general, one should not try to make behavioral traits go away because that is not really possible. However, what can be very successfully is to recognize traits that cause problems and then learn ways to deal with them. For instance if one is highly intolerant of uncertainty then they need to learn to recognize this, learn how and under what circumstances this behavior becomes apparent, where and when it causes problems, and then how to take actions to avoid such problems. This may include such things as tolerating the feeling and then using rational thinking to select the best possible option, which may be the opposite what the anxious trait would suggest ("opposite emotion-action").

How do these personality traits interact with each other and with other factors such as society and culture, family, stress, and biology to form a person's character? There is a dynamic interaction between genetic predisposition and environment, with a lot of "shaping" happening within a family environment. A problem arises when there is a poor "goodness of fit," which can be seen in situations when parents feel and act in very different ways to how their child is driven to behave, which is when parents and child have different personality traits. These constellations can be very difficult to manage for everyone involved and require a very fine balance and much self-control to promote a well functioning family environment.

As the definition implies traits cannot be changed. However, they are often magnified during the acute eating disorder when one feels vulnerable and has less ability to control one's feelings and behaviors. It would be helpful if we could pinpoint people at risk of developing eating disorders based on personality traits. However, this cannot be done reliably although the combination of anxious traits such as harm avoidance and intolerance of uncertainty as well as perfectionism could raise concerns that under certain conditions this could increase the risk for an eating disorder. I know a person who was seen by a therapist for anxiety when she was twelve years old. At the time she completed various assessments and the therapist predicted with "100% certainty" that she would have anorexia nervosa within the next few years. Now 5 years later she has not developed an eating disorder, although she still tends to be anxious. On the opposite side, as described above, there are children who develop anorexia within a few months after making changes with their eating. The maybe most important aspect to learn is to understand who we are, what our behavioral traits are, play to our strengths and work with the weaknesses in the best way possible. For parents I think it is important to be vigilant. Children usually do not grow out of problem behavior, rather they grow into them with increasing age, although they may look different when older. If there are behaviors that interfere with well being or normal social interactions, one should intervene or seek help rather sooner than later.

8. What About The Family?

The family was seen as the culprit in the earlier days of psychiatry in many cases. Children with schizophrenia or autism were thought to be from cold and un-empathic mothers. In the case of eating disorders it was long thought that those individuals who developed an eating disorder came from middle class families that could not provide for the needs of the child, as described above in the paragraph on Hilde Bruch. Over the past 20 years research on the neurobiology of eating disorders has made much progress and there are some who believe that it is merely a biologically driven illness. The truth may lie somewhere in between. Similar to many other psychiatric disorders, eating disorders are complex problems with biological, psychological and social factors. There is clearly no one type of family system that will drive development of an eating disorder, except maybe families with many other individuals with eating disorders and the children share the biological vulnerabilities and also see and learn those behaviors.

What often happens is that when an eating disorder is in full swing, the family hierarchy is turned upside down, the parents often lose control and the eating disorder is allowed to spin out of control, simply because nobody knows at that point how to best support the child. Reestablishing the normal hierarchy where the parents are in charge is a major goal in recovery and is reflected in the family based treatment approach. In this approach a key step is that the parents take control over eating and the adolescent does not have control over that aspect of life for some time.

There are a few important family dynamics that are true for some but not for all individuals with eating disorders. Those dynamics and mechanisms are based on psychodynamic family work including works from Bert Hellinger and others. I have personally used this knowledge to treat individuals with anorexia and bulimia nervosa where I thought the approach fit and found that this approach led to rather unexpectedly successful treatment outcomes. Importantly, this approach was not used alone, but in conjunction with and embedded in a highly structured treatment program that included nutritional rehabilitation.

One such dynamic applies to some with anorexia nervosa. In this dynamic the child is terrified of the idea that the father might "leave" the family. This can be a true danger of the divorce of the parents or can be just be a perceived danger of such a loss happening. The child then has the (typically subconscious) thought "rather I go than you." In other words, the child would rather die from anorexia nervosa than witness the father leaving the family. The eating disorder is often then a means of having the parents work together. The child (typically daughter) is very attached to the father but there is an imbalance and she needs to get closer to the mother.

Another dynamic applies to some with bulimia nervosa. In this dynamic a divorce has often already happened. The child is relatively close to the mother but the imbalance is in the opposite direction and she has to get closer to the father, who is often despised because of the divorce. These can be powerful dynamics to be explored in psychotherapy but they clearly do not apply to everyone and one cannot assume any underlying family mechanism in the development of the eating disorder.

Because these dynamics are subconscious they need to be explored with great caution and the use in therapy needs to be carefully set up in order to be successful.

It is important to keep in mind that regardless of what family dynamics exist or existed, the eating disorder becomes its own self-reinforcing process and solving any family problems is typically not enough to resolve the eating disorder. There is usually still a long road ahead of the individual and the support system to help that person to re-habituate to eating.

There is one family "dynamic" though that I think is most important to highlight and that is whether the parents or guardian(s) of a child with an eating disorder can work together in the treatment process. It can be very difficult for parents who are separated or divorced to work together. I have seen parents where one person was not able or willing to sit in one room with the other parent, which destroys any united front against the eating disorder. The reality is that recovery in those situations becomes exponentially more difficult for the child and the family.

Many adults with eating disorders are married and may have a family. Here the eating disorder is managed but may at times exacerbate and disrupt the system. It may be most important that the partner is closely involved in helping the loved one in battling the disorder and learn to do "the right things" to help with meal planning, help with distraction or other skills to avoid binge eating or purging behaviors etc. Sometimes there is a dynamic of the "sick person" in the family and the spouse who is the savior or helper. Key here to understand is that recovery is hard and that there is always the danger that the supportive spouse could become an enabler of the eating disorder if not keeping firm limits when having to do meal support for instance. This can be exceedingly hard and draining and cause much strain on the relationship. On the other hand, it may be the only way out of the disorder and toward a truly better life.

9. The Impact Of Society And Culture

There is undoubtedly an important influence of society and culture on eating behavior as well as our ideal of body shape. Children nowadays start to talk about shape and weight in elementary school, which may in part also be triggered by the high rate of obesity and the attempts to prevent and reduce obesity. On the other hand one can argue that all children are exposed to some degree to media influence including an often unrealistic ("photo shopped") ideal of thinness, but only some develop an eating disorder. The very early reports of anorexia nervosa hundreds of years ago also suggest that such media influences may not be necessary to develop an eating disorder. All in all the influence of media messages does not necessarily cause the eating disorder but may be an important stepping-stone. What is probably the case is that for some, maybe kids who tend to have lower self esteem or feel socially less well connected, they may strive for this ideal in order to compensate for their perceived shortcomings. Others may be striving for excellence in sports and fitness, which may drive over-exercising and the start of an eating disorder. Many children or adolescents talk about the positive feedback they received after they lost weight, which in turn reinforced food restriction and weight loss, and may turn into excessive behaviors. Another problematic dynamic that one can see often is when kids try to be in good shape but this process is very hard because they are maybe objectively overweight and the messages via advertisements cause poor self image and self esteem and it becomes a self reinforcing cycle of self hatred and negative overall self perception.

There are also various "fads" or "eating trends" that could lead someone into an eating disorder. Our society in general pays nowadays much attention to health and we hear literally every day reports what may be "good" or "bad" for our health. Lots of diet advice comes through the public media including potential benefits from eating gluten free, low fat, paleo (eating unprocessed foods), carbohydrate free, etc. For individuals who are genetically vulnerable, such diets could be promoting the development of an eating disorder.

Everyone is different and has a different story how she or he got into an eating disorder. However, the more comfortable a person feels about herself, the better the self esteem and the better the feeling one can manage the daily tasks and stressors in life, the less likely it is that messages from the media or society about an excessive thin-ideal can influence that person and drive unhealthy behavior.

10. Eating Disorders and the Brain

Brain imaging provides a "window" into the living human brain and may help us understand mechanisms that may cause eating disorders. It took millennia from the first humans to just decades ago when we were able to study how brain circuits get activated in the living human brain when we think, plan, make decisions or

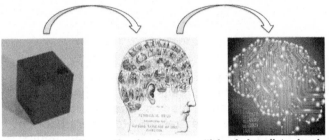

Figure 10.1. From the brain as a "black box" to brain regions that drive behaviors, and understanding now brain function as networks of interacting areas via neural connections and neurotransmitters.

prepare for action. This knowledge about specific regions and their interactions can be used to test behaviors that are linked to for instance an eating disorder. We try to understand how brain circuits are different in those conditions and that in turn may help us to understand underlying mechanisms. Only if we know how the brain works differently in eating disorders then we can work on specific interventions to improve treatment and make recovery more successful.

Dr. Guido K.W. Frank

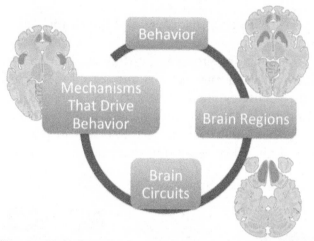

Figure 10.2. Research uses models of behaviors, brain regions and circuits that connect those regions. Using those models one can test how illness behaviors are related to altered brain function in order to understand biological mechanisms that drive behavior.

Basics of Brain organization

The brain, protected by the skull, is organized in specific brain regions or "lobes" that have special functions and each of those lobes has specific functions. The frontal lobe is important for decision-making. The temporal lobe contains the hippocampus, which organizes memory, and around the central sulcus is an area where we feel things ("sensory perception) or use those areas to move our limbs ("motor regions).

The occipital lobe is best known for its function in vision, and the cerebellum aids in motor function and balance. Each of those lobes then has an outside layer, the cortex, called gray matter. There are the cells located that process our thinking, feeling etc. Below the cortex is the white matter, massive fiber bundles that connect the gray matter with other lobes or deeper sitting structures, such as the basal ganglia, the brain stem and the spinal cord.

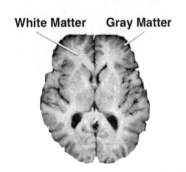

Figure 10.3. Basic brain organization.

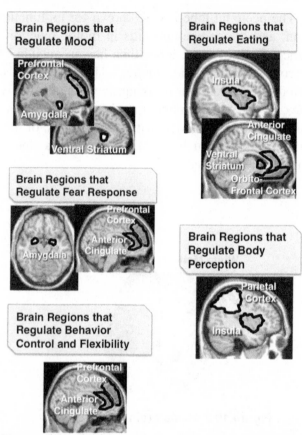

Figure 10.4. Brain regions and their associated functions.

Obviously, we cannot simply open up a living person's brain to study its function so indirect measures have been developed. Those are brain imaging "tools" that can be used to study the brain. To study brain gray and white matter volumes, magnetic resonance imaging

(MRI) is commonly used. The MRI machine is a big magnet that can measure brain structure and function because each part of the brain is a bit different in terms of how magnetic it is. Using MRI, we can also measure cortical thickness (how thick the gray matter is), surface area of the brain, as well as integrity and connectivity of white matter tracts, that is whether there is indication of damage to the white matter fibers and how many fibers connect the different brain regions.

What we are interested in is brain function and how the brain works under certain conditions. In this research effort we have participants perform tasks while their brain is scanned, in order to learn about how activity in brain regions is associated with certain behaviors and how a brain of someone with an eating disorder for instance works maybe differently compared to someone without an eating disorder.

The now most commonly used technique to study brain function (hence so called *functional* brain imaging) is functional magnetic resonance imaging (fMRI), which measures changes in local blood flow. Positron emission tomography (PET) and single photon emission computed tomography (SPECT) use radioactive ligands that distribute throughout the brain. Those methods can provide information about regional cerebral glucose metabolism or distribution of neurotransmitter receptors, receptors for brain chemicals such as serotonin or dopamine.

Brain volume

Research on brain structure in eating disorders has been inconsistent, with early studies suggesting reduced total gray matter and white matter volumes, and reduced or normal total brain tissue volumes after recovery. However, what we have learned over the past few years is that brain volume can change relatively quickly in response to fasting or overeating. It is therefore possible that many or most of those studies reported the effects of starvation and malnutrition, as opposed to alterations in brain volume that might have something to do with someone getting an eating disorder in the first place, or why it is difficult for someone to overcome an eating disorder.

In an effort to avoid the effects of acute starvation, malnutrition and dehydration we recently studied a sample of currently ill eating disorder individuals who had been in highly supervised treatment including a fixed meal plan for between 1 and 2 weeks and thus were nutritionally highly controlled. In addition, we controlled for age, depression, anxiety, medication-use and brain volume. We found that brain gray matter volume could identify shared abnormalities among eating disorder groups but also distinguish anorexia nervosa from bulimia nervosa. This sample of individuals with restricting type currently ill or recovered anorexia nervosa, ill bulimia nervosa and healthy control women showed increased gray matter volume of a part of the brain that is called the medial orbitofrontal cortex' gyrus rectus. That is a part of the frontal lobe and right between the eyes. This part is important for processing how much we eat, but also for decision making in general. Here our brain computes how much something is worth to us. In addition, ill and recovered individuals with anorexia nervosa had increased right, while individuals with bulimia nervosa had increased left gray matter volumes in the insula compared to healthy controls. The insula is on the side of the frontal cortex and here we process taste. In the insula we taste sweet, sour, salty and bitter and from there the information is transmitted to other brain regions. We also studied *adolescents* with anorexia nervosa and controls, with similar methods. Adolescents with anorexia nervosa showed greater left orbitofrontal and right insular volumes compared to controls similarly to the adults with anorexia nervosa. A recent study in obesity from our group suggests in contrast reduced orbitofrontal cortex gyrus rectus volume.

The orbitofrontal cortex is important in food intake control, telling us when to stop a certain type of food, regulating so-called sensory specific satiety. It is possible that larger orbitofrontal gyrus rectus in EDs is associated with stronger sensory experience of food and maybe also other salient stimuli, which could drive food avoidance. In fact, the medial orbitofrontal cortex has previously been associated with food avoidance and this region therefore could be a key structure in eating disorders. With respect to the left insula, this region receives information on gastric distention, which is how "full" someone feels after eating. Thus, altered insula size could interfere with normal interoception in bulimia, which may have a role in a reduced ability to sense "fullness" or satiation during a binge, but guilt is experienced and may trigger the urge to purge after excessive food intake. In healthy controls left sided anterior and posterior insula activation was associated with gastric distension and this was mediated by the body mass index, supporting the idea that alterations in the left insula could indeed contribute to inadequately feeling full and interfering with meal termination. *Right* anterior insula has been associated with self-recognition, the "abstract representation of oneself" and interoceptive awareness, and a fixed perception of being fat while severely underweight in anorexia nervosa could thus be related to right sided increased, abnormal anterior insula volume.

Importantly, these and other data suggest that when studying currently ill eating disorder individuals, it is imperative to control for nutritional state as well as comorbidity and medication use in order to be able to get more consistent results as well as identify brain alterations that are important for relevant eating disorder behavior as opposed to results that are mostly related to quickly changing effects of starvation. Controlling for those effects is not only important for volumetric studies, but new research also indicates that this affects studies on brain activity and function.

Brain function with focus on taste-reward processing

Food intake is driven by a complex interplay between cognitive, emotional and energy homeostasis maintaining mechanisms between brain and body. There is a cognitive or cephalic phase that involves desire or craving, as well as a consummatory phase involving the hedonic experience. These mechanisms were then further described as dopamine function associated "wanting" (drive to approach a reward), and "liking" (hedonic experience during food consumption) associated with opioid system activity. Those processes are regulated by the brain reward system, which integrates more basic metabolic hunger signals with higher order processing of taste and cognitive-emotional factors that drive whether we approach or not approach food stimuli.

Important brain regions that regulate those processes are the insula as the primary taste cortex and central gateway to the dopaminergic basal ganglia and midbrain, to higher order brain centers including the prefrontal and cingulate cortex that integrates cognition and emotions, the orbitofrontal cortex, which determines when to stop eating a type of food, and the amygdala that associate stimuli with emotional experience and that are thought to modulate dopamine circuitry in midbrain and striatum.

Dr. Guido K.W. Frank

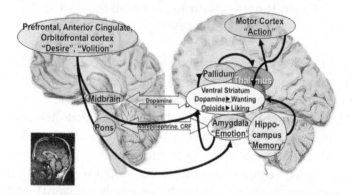

Figure 10.5. A schema for the brain reward system. In prefrontal cortex, anterior cingulate and orbito-frontal cortex we "create" thoughts and desires ("I want to eat"); from there activation goes to the ventral striatum to motivate action ("wanting" via dopamine), which is aided by memory via the hippocampus and emotional association from the amygdala; then activation in the motor cortex leads to "action" ("reaching for a slice of pizza"); then eating leads to enjoyment ("liking"), processed via opioids.

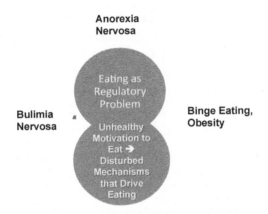

Figure 10.6. Individuals with eating disorders show a discrepancy between what a person is motivated to eat versus what the normal body needs to survive. Anorexia nervosa is associated with a low motivation or drive to eat while the body would need much more, in bulimia nervosa there is frequently low motivation to eat but intermittently excessive eating, and in obesity and binge eating there is a high internal drive to eat food, more than the body would need.

Several studies investigated brain taste-reward circuits in eating disorders. Individuals recovered from anorexia nervosa showed lower functional brain response to *repeated* but increased response to *randomly* given sweet taste stimuli (participants lie in a MRI scanner with tubes in their mouth and receive for instance sugar water). Those results in opposite directions suggest that unpredictable and predictable stimulus presentation activate differently circuits or neurotransmitter systems, when studying anorexia nervosa. Studies using monetary reward stimuli (playing a game where one can win money during brain scanning) indicated that subjects who were recovered from anorexia or bulimia nervosa showed less of a distinction in brain response to gain versus loss, suggesting that there could be distinct reward circuit alterations depending on the saliency of the stimulus.

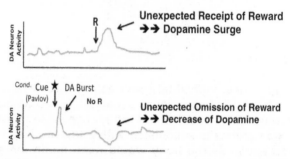

10.7. The principle of the prediction error / temporal difference model. Dopamine neuron activation occurs when there is unexpected receipt or unexpected omission of a salient stimulus.

Another approach is to pair unconditioned taste stimuli with conditioned visual or auditory stimuli and then at times omit an expected taste delivery or deliver a taste stimulus when none was expected. This leads to a discrepancy between reward anticipated or predicted and the reward actually received, the so called "prediction error", which is thought to reflect dopamine neuronal response. We have previously applied a prediction error taste-reward task using sugar solution and visual conditioned cues in anorexia nervosa and compared this group with obese individuals with the rationale that we might detect neurobiological alterations that lie on opposite ends, as suggested by basic research. We found that (insula and ventral striatum) prediction error response was greater or more sensitive in anorexia nervosa compared to controls, while obese individuals showed reduced response, supporting the notion that BMI and extremes of food intake may lead to adaptations of brain prediction error and thus dopamine brain response in humans. A similar study in bulimia nervosa found prediction error response reduced compared to controls but not reduced as much as in obesity. Bulimia nervosa's BMI typically lies between controls and obese subjects further supporting adaptive changes in dopaminergic pathways to food intake. Those results of altered prediction error response across eating disorder groups are potentially mechanistically important, as specific dopamine receptors have been implicated, such as the dopamine D1 and D2 receptor, making those receptors potential treatment targets. Otherwise, the literature on taste-reward in bulimia nervosa is small. A small pilot study that found lower anterior cingulate activation after sucrose stimulation in individuals who had bulimic symptoms in the past, two studies in BN after recovery indicated increased brain response in that group compared to controls. One of those studies applied repeated fat and high viscous stimuli and reported increased activation in the anteroventral striatum, and a study that used a task with recurrent sweet taste solution delivery reported heightened anterior insula activation. Those studies suggested that repeated taste stimulation "excites" brain response in bulimia nervosa more than in controls, which could trigger binge eating.

We know little about reward processing in youth with eating disorders, and only one small study tested this system in adolescents with anorexia nervosa. In that study, adolescents with anorexia nervosa exhibited an exaggerated response to losses compared to wins, supporting the notion that anorexia nervosa is associated with heightened sensitivity to loss or punishment.

In contrast to studying taste stimuli that are limited to basic nutrients such as sugars, others have investigated complex taste and food stimuli. This may have the benefit to reflect more real life situations. On the other hand those stimuli may be more difficult to model with respect to the underlying neurobiology of taste pathways. The emotional or pleasantness value that individuals with eating disorders assign to a simple sugar solution tends to be similar to controls, while complex tastes such as highly palatable sugar-fat combinations could be associated with for instance higher fear in the eating disorder groups, which might confound the more basic taste pathway signal. One study for instance applied chocolate milk and found in restricting type anorexia nervosa in right amygdala and left medial temporal gyrus greater activation compared to controls when hungry contrasted against the satiety state. This could be a sign of heightened vigilance and anxiety in that group as having the chocolate milk indicates breaking the fasting and promote gaining weight by drinking the caloric beverage. Another study that applied chocolate milkshake found that women with bulimia nervosa had a positive correlation between negative affect and activity in the putamen, caudate, and pallidum, the basal ganglia, during milkshake anticipation. It was hypothesized that negative affect may increase the reward value of food in bulimia nervosa but it may be more likely that negative affect became a conditioned response to palatable food as it is associated with weight gain.

Summarizing, repeated and thus predictable application of basic sweet taste stimuli has been associated with reduced activation of taste-reward important regions such as insula and ventral striatum in anorexia nervosa, but increased activation in bulimia nervosa. Random application of those stimuli, however, has shown opposite results. This may suggest that there may be an interaction between conscious cognitive-emotional and more unconscious biological mechanisms that drive food approach and eating. A potential explanation here may be that during repeated taste application the persons with anorexia nervosa "prepare" themselves and control brain response in order to avoid too high stimulation; however, during the random application this control is not possible and an enhanced responsiveness in anorexia nervosa is coming to light. In bulimia nervosa, a reduced biological responsiveness to taste stimulation becomes obvious during random application, while the repeated taste stimulation could kindle and enhance the low baseline response, maybe through the repeated hedonic experience.

Networks

A variety of functionally connected brain networks have been identified that drive behavior, including the default mode network (DMN), salience network (SN) and executive networks for higher order processing as well as sensory and sensorimotor (SMN) networks for "lower-order" function (7, 8). For the most part so called functional connectivity studies have investigated those networks, that is the synchronicity of various brain regions was tested and then speculated on the functional networks involved. One study found decreased activity within the visual network in ill and recovered anorexia nervosa compared to controls, but also found increased somatosensory network activity in anorexia nervosa. This is in line with a recent study that found altered connectivity in visual pathways when viewing human bodies, overall suggesting visual network disturbances that could be related to altered body self perception. A study in recovered anorexia nervosa showed increased DMN activity, and in a study that contrasted anorexia nervosa, bulimia nervosa and controls, patterns of connectivity between insula and frontal brain regions distinguished groups during a visual food cue task. A recent study found alterations in connectivity patterns within the cerebellum in anorexia and bulimia nervosa compared to controls, but the meaning or functional implications are uncertain.

Similarly, a study in a small sample of individuals with anorexia nervosa indicated reduced brain connectivity in anorexia nervosa during rest in the frontal cortex in regions that contribute to cognitive control. That study further indicated an interesting distinction, that is from the inferior frontal gyrus to the cingulum decreased, but to the orbitofrontal cortex increased connectivity in the anorexia nervosa group. A study from our group found reduced SN activity during taste stimuli delivery in ill and recovered anorexia nervosa compared to controls, which could be a trait-related biomarker or illness remnant altering the drive to approach food. We also found reduced DMN and SMN activity but in ill anorexia nervosa only, suggesting state-dependent abnormalities, possibly related to altered interoception and body image in anorexia nervosa when underweight, but remitting following recovery.

Taken together, this literature is still very small, but it seems that visual and salience network alterations could be involved in the pathophysiology of eating disorders, as a state dependent factors or even as biological trait.

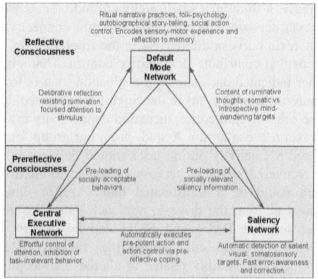

Figure 10.8. A model for brain network interactions. From Allen and Williams, 2011

Brain Neurotransmitters

Neurotransmitter receptor imaging studies assess the "functional availability" of neurotransmitter receptors in the brain. Neurotransmitters, or "brain chemicals" such as serotonin (5HT), dopamine (DA), opioids, etc. act on so called receptors in the brain, that are small molecular structured that then send an electrical impulse after activation, which leads to behavior. For those studies, a radioactive substance, a "ligand" that binds to a specific receptor type, gets injected into the person's blood and then its distribution can be measured in the brain, giving an indication of receptors available. Several studies have advanced our knowledge over the past decade, although there has also been a limitation in available receptor ligands that can be used in humans and thus limited the ability to characterize comprehensively neurotransmitter receptor systems. Serotonin (5-HT) 1A receptor binding was found to be elevated across most brain regions in ill restricting and binge eating/purging type anorexia nervosa as well as binge eating/purging type anorexia nervosa after recovery. In contrast, one study in recovered restricting type anorexia nervosa showed normal brain 5-HT1A binding. In addition, reduced 5-HT2A binding in frontal, parietal, and occipital cortices in ill and recovered anorexia nervosa was found. In summary, after recovery, 5-HT1A receptor binding seems to differentiate anorexia nervosa subtypes, whereas 5-HT2A receptor binding is reduced in both restricting and binge eating/purging anorexia nervosa in various brain regions. Since these disturbances occur after recovery, they may reflect either trait disturbances or scars from the illness. Various studies could correlate 5HT receptor availability or the interaction between 5HT and DA receptors with harm avoidance, a behavioral correlate of anxiety, but the exact mechanisms or functional relationships need further study.

Brain Neurotransmitter Receptors

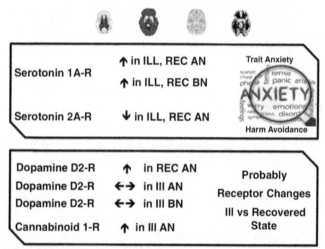

Figure 10.9. Summary of neurotransmitter receptor studies in eating disorders. Serotonin receptor alterations have been associated with high anxiety in eating disorders. Overall the studies have been small, which limits the conclusions that can be drawn.

In bulimia nervosa 5-HT transporter (a receptor that regulates how much serotonin is in the synaptic cleft) binding was reduced in thalamus and hypothalamus, but 5-HT1A receptor binding was increased in medial prefrontal cortex, posterior cingulate, and parietal cortex. After recovery, bulimia nervosa had increased 5-HT1A binding compared to controls, and 5-HT1A binding in bulimia nervosa predicted inhibition. The dynamics between 5-HT receptor expression and synaptic 5-HT are not well understood, but reduced 5-HT2A binding in recovered bulimia nervosa subjects may be related to higher level of endogenous 5-HT in the synaptic cleft, or a down-regulation of the receptor.

A group of women recovered from anorexia nervosa showed increased DA D2/D3 receptor binding in the antero-ventral striatum, while decreased DA D2/D3 receptor binding was found in obesity. Those findings support the possibility that D2/D3 receptor binding may be inversely related to weight and eating, with restricting-type anorexia nervosa on one end and obesity on the other end of the spectrum. It is possible that increased DA D2/D3 receptor binding in anorexia nervosa is part of underlying mechanisms why individuals with anorexia nervosa are able to resist eating. It is worth noting that food restriction sensitizes D2/D3 receptors while excessive food intake down-regulates DA D2 receptors in animal models and similar mechanisms in anorexia nervosa or obesity could complicate recovery. A very recent study found that individuals with bulimia nervosa had a trend of lower DA D2/3 receptor binding in the striatum as well as less DA release compared to controls in response to methylphenidate application. While overall this body of research is small, it suggest that food restriction in anorexia nervosa may increase and episodic binge eating in BN or chronic overeating in obesity could reduce DA receptor activity or expression.

Brain Imaging Summary

Brain imaging will continue to be an important tool for brain research in eating disorders, although it is not ready yet as a diagnostic tool or for directing intervention. The studies conducted over the past decade have furthered our understanding of the pathophysiology of eating disorders in various ways. First, studies show that it is highly important to carefully select study participants, and control for nutritional status and comorbid conditions in order to identify brain regions that have functional importance and are not only a reflection of dehydration and malnutrition. From the aggregate of studies there is now strong evidence that reward pathways may have a central role in eating disorder pathophysiology. The orbitofrontal cortex and connecting fibers are altered across eating disorders and a larger volume of the orbitofrontal cortex could contribute to being able to stop eating before the physiological need is met, supporting ongoing or intermittent food restriction in anorexia nervosa or bulimia nervosa, respectively. Another key region is the insula, which is altered across a variety of structural and functional studies. Those regions are part of the taste-reward system supporting the evidence that reward pathways are implicated in eating disorders. Within that network, it is possible that anorexia nervosa is associated with heightened and bulimia nervosa and obesity with reduced dopamine related circuit responsiveness. Importantly, those results could point toward future pharmacological interventions, as specific DA receptors are associated with brain reward function.

Future research will have to combine neurotransmitter as well as fMRI studies in order to better integrate behavior, molecular targets and neuronal activity and function. Results from network connectivity studies are few and variable, but there seems to be also at least some convergence pointing to altered reward circuit function. Specifically those studies indicate differences in salience network activity compared to controls, which may interfere with a normal orientation toward food related stimuli, as opposed to for instance focus on academic study and achievement and overriding such basic needs.

Genetics

When about 20 years ago, the genetic revolution was up and coming it seemed that we would soon know all about the genetic code of diseases and disorders and would then quickly develop interventions. Unfortunately, it turned out though that nature is more complicated and while we know a general genetic code of our DNA, we do not know much about how genetic mechanisms exactly drive psychiatric disorders. None of the available methods, including linkage, candidate gene or genome wide association studies (GWAS), has yielded conclusive results at this point.

"One gene-One Disease Model"

Linkage analysis - "To obtain a crude chromosomal location of the gene or genes associated with a Phenotype"

If **A is the disease gene** and B and C are genetic markers, recombination is likely to occur much more frequently between A and C than it is between A and B. This allows the disease gene to be mapped relative to the markers B and C.

Candidate Gene Analysis -

Gene 1   Gene 2

Choose candidate genes based on a biological system or quantitative trait locus (QTL) information → a section of DNA (the locus) that correlates with variation in a phenotype "quantitative trait"), e.g. learning, body weight, etc. The QTL typically is linked to, or contains, the genes that control that phenotype.

Psychiatry → Complex behaviors are influenced by **tens if not hundreds or thousands of genes →** search for those various genes across the genome.

Genome Wide Association Studies (GWAS)

...is an examination of many common genetic variants in different individuals to see if any variant is associated with a trait.

... typically focuses on associations between single-nucleotide polymorphisms (SNPs) and traits like major diseases.

Epigenetics

...the study of how the environment influences gene expression, e.g. DNA methylation alters gene expression

Figure 10.10. Genetic analysis methods are complex. They have evolved from the idea that one gene causes a disease, to models where multiple genes contribute to developing an illness. Furthermore, our genetic code is mostly stable, however how this code is used to produce proteins in the body changes depending on influences from the environment and life experiences.

The most progress has been made in schizophrenia but convincing or disease relevant discoveries in eating disorders have not been easy to make. Nevertheless, eating disorders run in families and there should be a genetic underpinning for this association. What most likely complicates the discovery of genes underlying eating disorders is that they are maybe more complex than other disorders including the self-driven nature of the disorder. When a person develops schizophrenia then the disorder just comes on, there may be some environmental factors such as living in a densely populated urban setting but overall it is a disease process that is not driven by the person's own doing. In the eating disorders field things are different and fear and anxiety may drive the eating disorder together with influences from the environment and media, which then interact with genetic vulnerability. Thus there are most likely aspects of the disorder where genes are involved, but to tease those apart from other factors will require much more study.

11. The Perfect Storm – A Developmental Model for Eating Disorders

Here we want to take the various biological, psychological and social factors into account and present a proposed model for developing an eating disorder (9).

We propose that individuals who will develop an ED are born with biological traits such as disposition to heightened anxiety, increased sensitivity to salient stimuli, as well as a larger (anorexia and bulimia nervosa) or smaller (binge eating disorder, obesity) orbitofrontal cortex, which could alter the individual's ability to stop eating when physiologically no more food is needed. In addition, we propose that eating disorders are associated with dopamine circuits that are less stable during development and might adapt too quickly to environmental influences. Individuals who develop AN may be particularly sensitive to times when there is less food eaten, such as skipping meals when having a busy schedule, voluntary fasting for spiritual reasons, or changing eating behavior in an attempt to eat "healthier", etc. In those individuals the dopamine system might get overly sensitized to a point where stimulation is perceived as excessive as opposed to driving healthy eating. This together with anxiety and high cognitive control as typically seen in anorexia nervosa may lay the foundation for the disorder risk. Bulimia nervosa has also been associated with high cognitive control, anxiety, and sensitivity to salient stimuli; however, those individuals may be more sensitive to excessive food intake and desensitization of dopamine terminals. While individuals with bulimia nervosa often restrict food intake especially during the day, they also have times when they "have to give in" to the urge to binge and purge, and the desensitized dopamine system overrides the cognitive control and needs stimulation. We know little about binge eating disorder brain function, but based on our studies in obesity one could hypothesize that in this group dopamine circuits are easily desensitized to excessive food, and that paired with a less strong cognitive control mechanism could predispose an individual to have difficulty stopping eating, even when physiologically sufficient food has been eaten.

Specific environmental triggers then may set off active illness behavior. Such triggers may include either states of food restriction (travel, camp, busy schedule) or excessive food intake (holidays, frequently being exposed to buffet meals, familial habit to present large portions), which may interact with dopamine circuits that are vulnerable to the effects of high or low food intake. Another important factor in triggering dopamine system alterations is puberty. Estrogen has a variety effects on eating behavior via neurotransmitter function and may play an important role in ED risk. With menarche there is a surge in sex hormones including estrogen, which has profound effects on dopamine release. Eating disorders typically begin during the years of sexual maturation and around menarche, and estrogen – dopamine interactions could contribute mechanistically to their development. This change in estrogen mediated dopamine release could add to over-stimulation in anorexia nervosa and promoting aversive response to salient stimuli, but a dopamine system vulnerable to desensitization could down-regulate too strongly in response to the strong physiological dopamine release.

In some factors such as problems in family functioning, poor self esteem, and social pressure may drive altered food intake in response to those difficult situations that create negative emotions and heightened stress. Stress neurobiologically alters dopamine and opioid neurotransmission and affects eating behavior. Stress therefore could have an important mechanistic role in driving a person into eating disorder behaviors. The social pressure to be thin also creates stress but also frequently leads to positive feedback (psychological reward) from the environment after weight loss. This promotes more weight loss and potentially dopamine sensitization, but also stress because of increased fear of weight gain. On the other hand, weight gain in bulimia nervosa or binge eating disorder is frequently associated with negative feedback, this typically leads to lower mood, and eating is often used to handle stress from the sense of social inferiority.

Then after establishment of the eating disorder behaviors, a vicious cycle develops. Food restriction in anorexia nervosa reduces overstimulation but further sensitizes the dopamine system.

Predisposing Traits, "Biology"

- Anxiety, Sensitivity to Salient Stimuli
- Altered Orbitofrontal Cortex Mediated Satiety
- Unstable Dopamine Circuits

AN: ↑ Cognitive Control
        DA Sensitizes to Food Restriction

BN: ↑ Cognitive Control
        DA Desensitizes to Excessive food

BED: ↓ Cognitive Control,
        DA Desensitizes to Excessive Food

Precipitating – Biologically

- Puberty
- Exposure to Food Restriction
- Exposure to Excessive Food

Precipitating - Psychologically

- Family Function Causing Stress
- Poor Self Esteem Leading to Self Definition Via Body Weight
- Social Pressure Leading to Altered Food Intake

Perpetuating Vicious Cycle:

AN
- ↑ Food Restriction Further ↓ DA Overstimulation

BN
- Cognition Drives Food Restriction and Purging
- Hyposensitive DA Circuits Drive Binge Eating

BED
- ↑ Food Intake Further Desensitizes DA Circuits, Leading to More Craving and Food Intake

Figure 11.1. From Frank, 2016, The Perfect Storm.

Those biological changes together with high fear of weight gain then creates a situation where the normal eating stimulating mechanisms fail and dangerous weight loss ensues. In bulimia nervosa, the high cognitive control paired with hyposensitive dopamine circuits may lead to episodic food restriction interrupted by binge eating and purging episodes. In obesity and maybe also binge eating disorder, high food intake further desensitizes dopaminergic circuits, resulting in even more food intake in order to satisfy the need for stimulation of this circuitry.

12. Criteria for Treatment, Levels of Care, Treatment Settings and Interventions

There is clearly no one way to overcome an eating disorder. In the past I have worked extensively with individuals who have recovered from eating disorders. In the group with bulimia nervosa about 50% said they became tired of the behavior and just stopped. The other half had a more protracted and difficult course to recovery. I believe this split reflects the more or less strong biological versus socio-cultural factors that drive the eating disorder. In the anorexia nervosa group it seemed that typically a dramatic or truly meaningful event happened that facilitated recovery. For instance, the person was "really" worried of dying, maybe because a friend had passed away from anorexia nervosa or they had to get hospitalized themselves for a life threatening complication of the eating disorder. Others may have fallen in love and the power of the romantic relationship helped with recovery. One person who I worked with wanted to join the army, therefore she gained just enough weight to get admitted and during basic training everyone had meals together and she got used to eating normally again. Many in the anorexia nervosa group had long courses of the illness and it often took much work to beat the fears of getting fat. The increased attention eating disorders have received over the past few decades has lead to earlier detection and intervention, which has been shown to improve treatment outcome. However, eating disorders continue to have highly increased rates of death compared to the general population, with chronic course, not living in a relationship and not completing treatment as recommended being predictors of earlier death (10). Thus, adequate intervention is clearly needed to improve outcome. There are some who with their own effort and maybe with the help of their family can recover without any professional help. Others are not able to do that and require treatment by professionals in fields including psychotherapy, psychiatry and nutrition. Again, the treatment should be tailored to the person's needs, depending on age, type of eating disorder, medical complications, comorbidity and support system.

Treatment Settings

There are typically 6 levels of care available for EDs: outpatient treatment (OTP), intensive outpatient treatment (IOP), partial hospitalization (PHP, most effective if administered for at least 8 hours/day, 5 days/week; less intensive care is demonstrably less effective(11)), residential treatment center treatment (RTC), specialized eating disorder focused psychiatric inpatient hospitalization treatment (IP) designed for both medical stabilization and acute stabilization of behavioral considerations; and inpatient medical care (IMC) focused primarily on medical stabilization. Level of care can be determined by a variety of factors, including medical status, suicidality, body weight, motivation to recover, co-occurring disorders, structure needed for eating and gaining weight, ability of the family to manage eating disorder behaviors, the ability to control compulsive exercising or urging behavior (laxatives and diuretics), and what treatment is available in a specific geographical region.

The American Psychiatric Association last published guidelines for care of patients with ED's in 2006 and in 2014 the American Academy of Child and Adolescent Psychiatry released practice parameters for children and adolescents (12). Research over the past decade, along with improvements in access to care, earlier identification of eating disorders, and a focus on evidence based care specifically for children and adolescents, have led to an emphasis on providing care in lower levels of care whenever possible. Inpatient medical, psychiatric and residential care for eating disorders are of very high cost when compared to PHP and outpatient interventions, without clear evidence of improved outcomes. For instance, one study compared PHP with IP care for adolescent AN and found one year after treatment no benefit of prolonged IP treatment over PHP after an initial 3 week hospitalization for medical stabilization. Another study that assessed adolescents with AN after one, two, and five years after treatment also did not find benefits from prolonged IP treatments, suggesting that IP is not a cost effective level of care.

For medical reasons, IMC is indicated for adult patients with a heart rate <40 bpm; blood, pressure <90/60 mmHg; glucose<60 mg/dl; potassium <3 mEq/L; electrolyte imbalance; temperature <97.0°F;

dehydration; hepatic, renal, or cardiovascular organ compromise requiring acute treatment; poorly controlled diabetes. For children and adolescents criteria have been slightly modified to a heart rate of close to 40, orthostatic blood pressure changes with >20 bpm increase in heart rate or >10 mmHg to 20 mmHg drop, a blood pressure <80/50 mmHg, hypokalemia, hypophosphatemia or hypomagnesaemia.

IP (medical or specialized eating disorder psychiatric units) is also usually indicated when BMI (weight in kg / height in m^2) is <16 in adults or <75% of expected weight for age, or when there is acute weight decline with food refusal despite higher weight.

IP is also indicated if there is acute suicidality including a specific plan with high lethality or intent; admission may also be indicated in patients with suicidal ideas or after a suicide attempt or aborted attempt, depending on the presence or absence of other factors modulating suicide risk. Suicide risk assessment is a complex problem and specific guidelines should be adhered to for this assessment. A general psychiatric inpatient unit may be needed for patients with significant suicidal ideation or suicidal or self-injurious behavior, in case that cannot be handled on the eating disorder inpatient unit. Motivation to recover, also described as "readiness for change" (RFC), includes cooperativeness, insight, and ability to control obsessive thoughts and respond to supervision and support and has been linked to positive treatment outcomes. The determination of level of motivation or RFC needs to be assessed carefully, taking each patient's specific background into consideration. OTP is often adequate for patients with fair-to-good motivation, fair motivation is adequate for IOP, and partial patient motivation defined by patients who are cooperative but preoccupied with intrusive, repetitive thoughts >3 hours/day and having difficulty interrupting eating disorder behaviors PHP is more likely to be the most effective and least restrictive level of care necessary. RTC may be indicated for patients with low motivation and RFC who have not been successful in other levels of care, including brief inpatient stabilizations. Patient with low / poor motivation are preoccupied with intrusive, repetitive thoughts which impact their behavior and require the external structure and constant supervision of a highly structured treatment environment. However, there are also questions that have been raised about RTC treatment. First, those centers are expensive and their quality of care is variable, and largely unregulated. Second, there are positive reports published on outcome from RTCs but there are no comparative studies with other treatment modalities. This has been especially brought to the forefront in the context of family based treatments as RTC are frequently far from home and the families may be less involved than necessary. In general, RTC treatment may be particularly suitable for patients with severe comorbid conditions, chronic self harm, and personality disorders. IP is indicated for patients whose medical condition or intensity of behaviors require 24 hour care before transition to PHP or OTP. Patients with higher levels of awareness, insight, and motivation are likely to improve more quickly and accept interventions and support with less distress.

Comorbid conditions including substance use have to be assessed individually for each patient and taken into consideration for determination of level of care.

For patients with severe food avoidance behaviors, nasogastric feeding may be necessary (a tube is placed through the nose that leads into the stomach for liquid feedings), which is usually initiated during IP medical, psychiatric or on a specialized eating disorder unit. OTP and IOP are often adequate for patients who are able to eat with family support. PHP is useful for stabilizing eating disorder behaviors when the family is able to provide support and supervision in the evenings, and for supporting the transition to home and school. It is critical to carefully evaluate the ability of parents to support and actively participate in treatment for children and adolescents. Families who are not willing or able to participate in care are more likely to require more extended interventions and higher levels of care than families who are motivated and engaged in treatment of the child with an eating disorder.

Patients with severe purging behaviors who need supervision during and after all meals and in bathrooms, who are unable to control multiple daily episodes of purging that are severe, persistent, and disabling, despite appropriate trials of outpatient care need IP level of care, even if routine laboratory test results reveal no obvious metabolic abnormalities. If there are no significant medical complications from purging behavior, such as electrocardiographic or other abnormalities, suggesting the need for hospitalization, then patients may be managed on OTP, IOP or PHP levels of care. Key is that the cycle of binge eating and purging behavior is interrupted for some time, which has strong psychological impact.

Severe environmental stress or family conflicts can make higher levels of care of care necessary. Another reason for higher level of care can be when a patient has to travel out of state for a specialized eating disorder treatment program and RTC or IP are the only viable alternatives.

For bulimia nervosa, in general, outpatient treatment is recommended, except when there are complicating factors (e.g., serious general medical problems, suicidal behavior, psychosis) or severe disabling symptoms that do not respond to outpatient treatment. A study compared two options for such patients: IP and PHP treatment. In that study, 55 patients with severe BN were randomly assigned to either one of those settings. At 3 months post-treatment, both treatments were associated with reduced general and specific pathology (13). While more deterioration in bulimic symptoms occurred following IP than day clinic treatment, the results overall were found to be comparable.

A common problem is insurance coverage. My personal recommendation is to work as much as possible with insurers and demonstrate that good treatment is not only in the best interest of the patient but also of the insurance company as relapse and readmissions will cost more than a successful treatment course. In that context it is important to strive for the least restrictive treatment setting possible and focusing on fast reintegration of the patient into normal life and society. In the next chapter we describe an approach for children and adolescents that involves the family from beginning of treatment and that is geared toward a total treatment duration of 5 weeks.

Specific Treatments, "Interventions"

Fitzpatrick and Lock (2011) and Hay and Claudino (2012) summarized treatment studies and their likelihood of benefit for recovery.

The Table 12.1. indicates that especially for anorexia nervosa the treatment options are very limited, and especially medication options that reliably improve the condition are lacking. For bulimia nervosa (Table 12.2.) there are several medications as well as psychotherapy helpful.

Likely to be Beneficial - Anorexia Nervosa	
Re-feeding	Rigaud et al, 2007

Unknown Effectiveness	
Atypical Antipsychotics	Mehler-Wex et al, 2008
Benzodiazepines	No Systematic Studies
Cyproheptadine	Halmi et al, 1986
Serotonin Reutake Inhibitors	Claudino et al, 2010
Psychotherapy	Hay et al, 2010
Inpatient vs. Outpatient Tx	Bulik et al, 2007
Estrogen for osteoporosis	Klibanski et al, 1995

Likely to be Ineffective or Harmful	
Older Generation Antipsychotics	Reilly et al, 2000
Tricyclic Antidepressants	Claudino et al, 2010

Table 12.1. Treatment studies in anorexia nervosa; Tx, treatment. Clinical Evidence, Fitzpatrick and Lock, Anorexia Nervosa, 2011

Likely to be Beneficial -   Bulimia Nervosa

Cognitive Behavioral Therapy (CBT)	Hay et al, 2007
SSRIs (FLXT, Citalopram, Sertraline)	Shapiro et al, 2007
Monoamine Oxidase Inhibitors	Bacaltchuc, 2002
Tricyclic antidepressants	Shapiro et al, 2007
(desipramine / imipramine)	

Unknown Effectiveness   Bulimia Nervosa

Cognitive Behavior Therapy or Exposure & Response Prevention	Hay et al, 2007
Interpersonal Psychotherapy	NICE, 2004
Guided Self Help CBT	Bailer et al, 2004
Dialectical Behavioral Therapy	Hay et al, 2007
Hypnotherapy	Griffiths et al, 1994
Motivational Enhancement	Treasure et al, 1999
Pharmacotherapy + CBT	Shapiro et al, 2007
Mirtazapine	No Systematic Studies
Reboxetine	No Systematic Studies
Venlafaxine	No Systematic Studies
Topiramate	Arbaizar et al, 2008

Table 12.2. Treatment studies in bulimia nervosa; FLXT, fluoxetine. Clinical Evidence, Hay and Claudino, Bulimia Nervosa, 2011

New treatment interventions and comparative effectiveness

A variety of other studies that have been reported. A few studies assessed the effects of nasogastric feedings in open trials. In one trial anorexia nervosa patients were randomly assigned to a tube-feeding group (n=41) or a control group (n=40). After 2 months, weight gain was 39% higher in the tube-fed group and binge-eating episodes were lower. Furthermore, the tube-fed group had a longer relapse-free period after discharge (34.3±8.2 weeks vs. 26.8±7.5 weeks). In another study (14), adult outpatients with anorexia or bulimia nervosa were randomly assigned to 2 months of cognitive-behavioral therapy (CBT) alone (n=51) or CBT plus tube feeding (n=52). CBT plus tube feeding lead to more rapid and frequent abstinence from binge eating and purging, more improvement on depression and anxiety, and patients reported better quality of life. A 1-year follow up further supported those results. BMI for patients in the tube feeding plus CBT arm was 18.2±3.3, and the analysis did not separate normal-weight patients with bulimia nervosa from patients with binge-eating purging type anorexia nervosa. However, in general, nasogastric tube feeding is not recommended for normal weight patients.

A recently developed treatment modality, "enhanced" CBT, which includes aspects of interpersonal therapy (IPT), was applied to 125 patients at a public outpatient clinic. Reportedly two-thirds of those who completed treatment (and 40% of the total) achieved partial remission. However, only 53% completed the treatment.

Medication use in anorexia nervosa has generally not been effective for weight gain, but a review of four randomized controlled trials and five open-label trials suggested that olanzapine, quetiapine, and risperidone may improve depression and anxiety. In another study that assigned 23 outpatients with AN to 8 weeks of olanzapine (2.5 mg/day, up to 10 mg/day as tolerated) or to placebo, patients receiving olanzapine showed a small (1 BMI point) but significant gain in BMI. However, others found no differences in percentage change in median body weight, rates of weight gain, or improvement in psychological measures 5 or 10 weeks after a small single-site, randomized, controlled trial of olanzapine versus placebo in 15 out of 20 adolescent females who completed the study. Another atypical antipsychotic, risperidone was studied in a double-blind randomized, controlled trial of 40 hospitalized adolescents with AN did not provide an advantage (average dose 2.5 mg/day, prescribed up to 4 weeks) over placebo for weight restoration. Based on our brain imaging studies we have started to use the dopamine D2 receptor partial agonist aripiprazole, but controlled studies are still lacking (15, 16).

A relatively new intervention that has been tested in youth with anorexia nervosa is Family-based treatment (FBT), a manualized and widely studied family intervention for adolescents with anorexia nervosa that stresses behavioral change by encouraging increased parental control over adolescent's maladaptive eating patterns. This intervention has shown higher rates of full remission and greater improvements eight to twelve months following treatment with regards to weight and ED pathology compared to family counseling and adolescent focused therapy, an individual outpatient intervention that is geared to improve eating symptoms and emotional tolerance. However, longer-term studies of the effectiveness of this intervention and other family treatments are limited. One five-year follow up study produced evidence suggesting when a high level of parental (specifically maternal) criticism is present, the use of separated family therapy, at least initially in treatment, is superior to using conjoint family therapy (as is traditional FBT). However, longer-term studies of the effectiveness of this intervention and other family treatments are otherwise limited. Importantly, new research now shows that in the general OTP setting FBT is more suitable for less severe cases of anorexia nervosa. And another very recent study that compared Parent-Focused Treatment and FBT for adolescent anorexia nervosa indicated that Parent Focused Treatment was more efficacious than FBT in bringing about remission but remission rates between the two therapies at follow-up were not statistically significant. Altogether, what type of psychotherapy is most specific and helpful for anorexia nervosa requires further study and may depend on the person's or family's individual situation.

13. Eating Disorder Treatment at Children's Hospital Colorado

In this chapter we would like to show how a specific treatment approach for adolescents may look like (17). We are incorporating the various forms of treatments that have been tested in eating disorders and have developed and comprehensive and patient and family oriented approach. This program includes both general treatment components with respect to nutritional rehabilitation, cessation of binge eating or purging etc., and by the same time the program is geared toward creating an individualized treatment that is tailored to a family's specific needs.

Our model is based on existing evidence emphasizing the important role of the family in child and adolescent onset eating disorders. The program is innovative and unique with families engaged daily in treatment, planning meals for their child in all levels of care, and participating in daily meals and program therapies. We provide consultation and support to other academic centers and private for-profit programs in efforts to improve their own approaches to care and program development. The emphasis of treatment is on helping families build the skills they need to help their child recover at home. Family Based Therapy (FBT) principles of empowering parents to effectively manage eating disorder symptoms are integral to our Parent Supported Nutrition (PSN) model of care (18-20). This approach in the treatment of child and adolescent onset anorexia nervosa has facilitated shifting to lower levels of care more quickly (PHP, IOP, OP). The emphasis in treatment is on parent training and skills for managing symptoms at home, which decreases the need for time away from the family and school.

Models of care for children and adolescents and adults with EDs vary widely across the United States and have typically emphasized residential treatment when a patient did not improve with outpatient care. Residential treatment center (RTC) care typically lasts 60-120 days, and the child is usually separated from their parents for the majority of the episode of care, creating challenges in the transition to home. There has been a significant shift to specialized outpatient care and day treatment, with inpatient care primarily used for medical stabilization. Lower levels of care are less disruptive to family and school functioning, more cost effective, and show similar or even improved outcomes supported by research.

For adults being in a RTC and away from the common home environment on the other hand can be freeing and help establish new behaviors. In Europe there are Psychosomatic Medicine Hospitals where patients are admitted from far away. Those environments can be quite helpful to provide a break from the daily stress at home and help establish new behavior patterns.

The specialized Eating Disorder Program in the Department of Psychiatry, Division of Child and Adolescent Psychiatry at the University of Colorado Anschutz Medical Campus, is embedded within the Children's Hospital Colorado and provides Specialized medical floor care, Inpatient Eating Disorder Unit (IP-EDU), PHP, IOP as well as OTP levels of care. The IP-EDU allows patients who still need nurse supervision, cardiac monitoring and low activity to be moved from the medical floor to the Eating Disorder Program quickly for start of and intensive family based therapy and parent involvement in care, while still medically stabilizing (improving heart rate and weight) to a point that the patient can safely sleep at home. This also allows to decrease cost of care, and improves the ability of the parent and child to work together during the day in our therapeutic milieu. Our parent supported recovery model, which includes parent skills training and parent supported nutrition (PSN) has decreased the number of admissions to the inpatient level of care, and decreased the length of stay in both inpatient and PDT levels of care. More patients are triaged to an outpatient family based therapy approach. Patients admitted to higher levels of care (day treatment or inpatient) average about 24 days in program over 5 weeks during which time the emphasis is on teaching parents meal planning and meal support skills as well as helping them learn and practice skills for more effective communication and improving the family structure. Patients can admit to any of the levels of care described below and level of care is determined through evaluation of medical, behavioral and emotional symptoms and the family's capability to participate in care. The emphasis for patients is on skill-building for tolerating the external structure and containment, which serves to interrupt the eating disorder behaviors and drives. We do not have a residential level of care, as our program emphasizes keeping children and adolescents with their families and in their home communities.

Intake and Treatment Process, and Levels of Care

1.<u>Initial Intake consultation and Triage:</u> A therapist from the eating disorder team and an adolescent medicine physician evaluate the child, gathering information about the current concerns, symptoms, contributing factors and determines if an eating disorder is likely. The parents are also interviewed and a team recommendation is discussed with the family for treatment interventions. Decision making about the most appropriate, least restrictive level of care is based on the following:

2.<u>Outpatient level of care:</u> Medically stable (HR > 50, weight > 80% IBW, electrolytes stable). Guardian able and willing to provide additional support and supervision and to be active in treatment. Able to weight restore over the first month of outpatient care.

3.<u>Inpatient Medical Unit admission:</u> Medically unstable, resting HR < 45 (HR < 35 at night), rapid weight loss, weight < 75% IBW, low kcal intake (< 1000 / kcal / day), risk of refeeding syndrome, need for bed rest to interrupt weight loss. Transition to inpatient EDU when HR is > 35 at night.

4.Inpatient Eating Disorder Unit admission: Resting HR 45-50 (HR > 35 at night), rapid weight loss or low kcal intake (1000 – 1500 kcals), weight < 80% IBW, significant resistance from child to parents' efforts to provide support and supervision. May also have safety issues such as suicidal ideation or self-injurious behaviors.

5.Extended Day Treatment Program (10-12 hours per day): More likely to be recommended if family has not been successful with outpatient care Medically stable but unable to interrupt eating disorder behaviors at home. Family and patient need more support and coaching to be successful at home.

6.Regular Day Treatment program (7 hours): partial success with PSN/FBT principles in outpatient level of care, medically stable, family and patient need more support and coaching to be successful at home.

7.Intensive Outpatient Program: Three times per week, 2.5 hours each session. Multifamily model of care, emphasis on continued recovery, relapse prevention and adapting PSN/FBT based principles to home and school, as well as supporting gradual transitions to normalized eating and activities. Families can enroll in IOP if they need more support than weekly outpatient therapy, or as part of the transition from higher levels of care.

At least one parent or guardian has to be involved in the treatment process. From the day of admission the treatment geared to give parents the tools to provide effective meal support for their child and be able to "bring EDU home", that is transfer treatment structure to home to support a successful and lasting recovery process.

Patients usually transition from higher to lower levels of care and discharge to outpatient treatment.

All patients have a primary therapist, a psychiatrist, a dietician, an assigned adolescent medicine doctor, as well as nursing staff and milieu therapists.

The program includes meals in program, supervised by staff with transition to meals supervised by parents or guardians. All families also receive family therapy as well as individual therapy for the child or adolescent. The treatment also includes multifamily groups, skills groups (for instance how to manage strong emotions), and art, yoga and movement therapy.

With the "bringing EDU home" concept, we aim for a fast reintegration into normal life including school and social contacts. Importantly, at the beginning of higher level of care treatment (inpatient, day treatment program) we start to look at set up of outpatient care when discharged in order to bridge this transition and a successful recovery.

14. Personal Accounts On Eating Disorders

1. My story

Ultimately, I think my eating disorder has to do with self-worth. It stems from a deep place of self-loathing. My earliest memory was sitting in a closet wishing that I could die. I am not sure how old I was but from a very young age I remember being unhappy, terrified, and guilty and bad. I was adopted as a baby at about 5 months old. I was left in a basket with a note with my name on the doorstep of a police officer, although I did not learn this until I was an adult. Sometimes I wonder if my life would have been different if I had know this growing up as a child? Would I feel less worthless, knowing that perhaps my birth mother *did* love me? In my mind I felt like I was worthless, I still do, and I think I always will. It is as if I am living on borrowed time that I should have been thrown out with trash. While I can only speculate what happened to me as a baby, I know it impacted me both in my personal views of myself and my world and also in my behaviors. On the outside, I had a pretty normal childhood. I grew up in a middle class family with parents that gave me every opportunity and made sure I was well taken care of. I was well behaved and exceled at school and had lots of friends. I went on trips and my parents took me to museums and ballet performances. While my family appeared 'normal' to everyone, there were also many secrets. For a period of time my father was an abusive alcoholic and he and my mom would fight often. My mom would sometimes take me to my grandparent's house when things were really bad, but the next day we would go home and things would go back to normal until the next time my dad got drunk. Although my father did recover from alcoholism, my parents continued to fight and were unhappy. Their situation taught me that appearances were very important and I learned how to keep secrets and hide my emotions. My adolescence was a series of secrets – self-mutilation and depression, unhealthy relationships with older men and the ultimate secret, my eating disorder.

When it was time to go to college I thought I was having a heart attack and went to the hospital. Most likely it was a panic attack because I have extreme separation anxiety and was going to a school out of state, but as soon as I got to college I wanted to 'get healthy'. I just started walking and then running every day. Eventually my knees hurt and I couldn't walk without pain, yet I ran more and more and that turned into cutting out foods, restricting calories, purging, which lead to even more restricting and more exercise. I lost half my body weight and was completely consumed with food and exercise. I 'cured' my obesity by developing anorexia. At the time I didn't realize how much it would ruin my life. After two years of self-deprivation and maladaptive behaviors, I was really sick. I did my first PHP treatment for 2.5 months and was able to learn the skills and restore some weight. I decided to take the semester after off and I did okay for a bit, but relapsed when I experienced the loss of a family member. A few months later I went back for another 1.5 months to the same PHP program. That summer I did well, I followed my meal plan, I didn't over exercise and didn't purge. My therapist in the program knew I loved science and told me that if I ever got a grant I could come back to the center and do research with her. So, as soon as I got back to college that is exactly what I did, I applied for a summer research grant, won the award and made my plans to go back and do research. Unfortunately I also fell back into the same patterns with my eating disorder as soon as I got back to school. I started at an IOP program and then had to end the semester early to go to a month-long inpatient program and then another IOP program. Despite my relapse this amazing person at my previous treatment center still allowed me to come back and do research. She believed in me and she gave me the chance and fought for me when no one else thought I was ready to be working in the field instead of being treated.

That summer was the best experience ever because my values changed. I no longer wanted to be the patient. I wanted to be on the other side, to be the one who had recovered. Sometimes I think about what my life would have been like had this woman not taken a huge chance on me, I was in a very vicious cycle and I needed something to get out of it. Sure, treatment taught me the tools I needed to learn to control my emotions and eat my meal plan and not let my anxiety get the best of me, but I think it was ultimately shifting my values that really helped me stay in recovery. I still struggle with my mood and anxiety and I still detest myself, but my eating is normal and I don't engage in the behaviors I did before. I am the happiest I have been and I don't keep secrets. Something I learned recently is that I am always going to hate myself, I am always going to feel undeserving and have low self-worth, but I don't have to let those feelings dictate how I live my life. I can hate myself but still love my life. Shifting focus away from myself and to the people in my life and the things I experience helped me stop the self-defeating behaviors.

I don't think any one thing caused my eating disorder. I think the combination of being abandoned as a child, growing up in an emotionally disconnected family, being different from my sister and struggling with weight were all environmental factors that when combined with my extremely detailed nature and sensitive personality created the perfect recipe for me to fall into anorexia during a stressful time, and once that got a hold of me, there was no turning back.

So how can someone become so obsessed and driven to lose weight and now not even really let those thoughts come into my mind? I think it has to do with my weight. Since puberty I was always heavy and once I gained back the weight the eating disorder thoughts got far less consuming. Sometimes in the summer I get this idea that I am going to lose weight so I start to workout more and then some weight comes off and at a certain point its like a switch turns on in my brain, I become obsessed with my weight, I get really vein and compare myself to everyone, I check my wrists and body parts to see if they change, I eat less and less and exercise more and more and skip meals and get these grandiose thoughts that I can lose 100 pounds and be thin again, but not be eating disordered. Fortunately, I know enough now about myself and my patterns that when I start going down that road I realize that as awful as it is I am not meant to be a thin person, its not my set-point, and so I am able to stop the cycle it gets out of control.

I think that many people who develop eating disorders are sensitive, sensitive to everything, we are detailed oriented, we have vivid memories, we take things very personally, and we are deeply impacted by the environment.

Low self-esteem may stem from being so sensitive because what people say or do really does affect us and goes deep into our core.

And, I think that there is something different in our brains that make us more susceptible to developing an eating disorder or relapsing. For me, just how changing my weight 10 or 15 pounds turns on or off the 'eating disorder switch' must mean something happens in my brain when I am not at my 'true' weight. My body dissatisfaction is never going to go away, I want to be thin and attractive and liked, but that innate drive to starve myself to get that way doesn't creep into my mind unless I start to lose weight either intentionally or just naturally.

Lessons I've learned:

As an adult I have learned that I cannot change my parents, they are who they are and they will always want things to appear perfect but I get a choice whether or not to be around them. I get a choice what parts of my life I share with them.

Like I said before, my self-worth will always be low, but instead of focusing on how much I hate myself, I focus on how much I love my life. I am surrounded by people who are caring and supportive and love what I do for a career. So my actions are focused on my life and not on myself.

Knowing now that I am very sensitive I am learning to be more gentle with myself. Things impact me more than other people and that isn't a bad thing, it just means I may need to take things a bit slower.

Finally, and most importantly, shifting my values away from my eating disorder helped me get out of the viscous cycle. Finding someone more important to me than losing weight slowly changed my values.

2. Anorexia.

A cold and clinical word, a passive acknowledgement swept under the table, a disease detached from the realm of consideration for many. But not for me.

I was twelve years old when my eating disorder first developed. I still vividly remember the first thought anorexia planted in my vulnerable and innocent mind: "You look so fat."

My eating disorder was notorious for inundating me with abusive insults like this for many years, but to this day, these words still punch a hole in my heart. In fact, the image still haunts me: that young, promising girl standing in a front of a dressing room mirror, gaping in horror at the prepubescent stomach protruding from her little blue bikini. What breaks my heart even more, however, is knowing that the light of that little girl's soul, which shone down with unbelievable brilliance upon herself and others, was diminished by darkness. The shadow of an eating disorder that she ended up falling a slave to-- almost.

In the grips of my eating disorder, recovery was something I had deemed to be impossible. I was drowning in the depths of the disease itself, yet I continued to believe that it was anorexia keeping me afloat. Despite that I was being pulled further beneath its waves, my disorder convinced me that recovering would be the anchor that would weigh me down, both figuratively and literally. While life was passing me by, I was slipping further into anorexia's abyss: an endless spiral of throwing away lunches, physically fighting with my parents, frantically running around school, doing hundreds upon hundreds of sit-ups at night, and pouring required supplement drinks down the kitchen sink to avoid consuming calories. Everyone and everything in front of me was rapidly emptying down the drain, yet I was too blinded by the E.D.'s lies to care. My classmates at school began to make comments about my abnormal behaviors and even noticed the emaciation ravaging my body. I had starved myself so brutally that it showed through the skin draping over my skeletal frame left like a blanket cast over a corpse. However, in my mind, the attention I was receiving was generating rapid popularity, which further fueled my eating disorder to do more. To my eating disorder, this mean an endless layer of rules that kept piling themselves on top of each other: to run 5 more laps around the school, to eat 100 less calories, to do 100 more crunches each night, to lose 10 more pounds. My life consisted of rigidity- of rituals and restrictions- that, if not exactly followed, resulted in self-inflicted punishment and explosive outbursts of guilt, shame, fear, and rage. As my physical state worsened, the fragile shell barely holding my life together continued to shatter even more, piercing my family and loved ones in its path. Even the activities and hobbies I had once enjoyed, such as playing soccer and writing poetry, were controlled by the wrath of the disease. I could no longer play the same game of soccer I once had a passion for because I spent the entire game sprinting up and down the sidelines and running in place on the field. I could no longer go to the mall or have sleepovers with my friends because of the intense food anxieties I had developed. I could no longer sit down and journal- or even write an essay assigned for school- because I believed that I would gain weight and become "fat" if I sat still. I could no longer go to a grocery store because being terrified of having to potentially eat the food surrounding me. I could no longer walk into a frozen yogurt shop without having a public outburst, stuck on the idea that just standing in the shop alone would cause people to associate me with being "fat." Every time I walked past a window or looked into a mirror, I saw a corpulent and disgusting creature staring back- not the sickly thin girl other people saw. My eating disorder had blindfolded and deluded me for so long into believing the thoughts it fed me that I could only see through its tunnel vision. These lies, along with a stream of others, corroded everything around me and consumed everything I did. My life had been torn off its axis in a matter of months, spinning out of control and colliding into more conflict as I desperately tried to cling onto the E.D.'s embrace.

On a snowy Sunday in the middle of April of 2013, not even 8 months after I was first diagnosed with anorexia, the last strand of sanity left in me finally snapped. At this point in time, any remains of my former self- the bright, thriving girl I was before- had been completely swallowed by my disorder's darkness. After learning that my soccer game had been cancelled due to snowy weather on that day, my eating disorder panicked. Furious that I was missing an opportunity to exercise, I refused to eat any food and began frantically running in place in attempt to burn as many calories as possible. As my mom pinned me down to prevent me from exercising in my feeble physical state, my eating disorder grew even more furious. I violently began kicking and clawing at her arms, desperately trying to tear myself from her grasp. However, with my mom's stubborn will to never stop fighting for me, she refused to let go. My eating disorder was relentless, screaming and trying to bargain its way into going on the exercise bike downstairs for 10 hours, a completely rational thought in my deranged state of mind.

Finally, my mom let me out of her sights for one moment to call my dad, who was on a business trip in Nevada. At this moment, I made a decision that changed my life forever. Too emotionally and physically exhausted to fight any longer, I attempted to end my life by jumping off of our second floor banister. Fortunately, my attempt was thwarted by my brother and mom, who caught me before I could succeed.

After spending a long and sleepless night in the Emergency Unit at Children's Hospital in Aurora, Colorado, the hospital I was driven to after my suicide attempt, I was admitted to the hospital's psychiatric ward. After spending four dark days there, I was finally transferred to the Eating Disorder Unit. At the time, the EDU was an inevitable sentence of imprisonment, an unavoidable abyss that my parents were forcing me to fall into. Little did I know, though, that it was the EDU that would set me free.

My journey through the eating disorder program at Children's Hospital was an experience unlike any I've ever had- one that was tumultuous and terrifying, painful and punishing, exhausting and emotional yet healing and hopeful all at the same time. To this day, I can still recall every detail of the EDU wing- the room I slept in during my first night of inpatient treatment, the long couch I lay on when I was getting my vitals checked, the large table I spent hours drawing and doing crafts at, and of course, every patient's worst nightmare- the cafeteria.

My treatment for my eating disorder began with the inpatient program at the EDU, which consisted of 24-hour treatment at the hospital for seven days of the week, in which I could only see my family during visiting hours and therapy sessions/ group treatment meetings. The duration of inpatient treatment not only depended on the state of a patient's physical health- which was determined by factors such as stability of my weight and vitals- but also by a patient's behavior. At the EDU, patients were vigilantly monitored at all times by counseling, nursing, psychiatric staff, who scanned for eating disorder behaviors like hawks on the prowl for prey. At every moment, even when I was using the restroom or taking a shower, a counselor was always watching to make sure that I was adhering to the unit's strict rules, which were designed to directly combat against the rules and rituals of my ED. Furthermore, during every snack or meal time, I was observed by a counselor who was there to for score my eating performance on the basis of the number of food avoidance behaviors that I engaged in, such as wiping, picking, or refusing food. Additionally, in order to eliminate disordered exercise and movement rituals, the EDU was extremely strict on patients who took unnecessary measures to move in attempt to burn calories. After initial redirection, these behaviors- which included taking longer routes to seats and shaking a leg, or walking at a quick pace- would result in receiving a shot of Boost supplement drink, a punishment that horrified patients because it meant consumption of extra calories. During my first few weeks of treatment, redirection for my movement behaviors came so frequently that my treatment team had to enact a "3-strike" system for me, which involved three chances to be redirected for movement before having to drink an ounce of Boost. With the implementation of this new plan, my eating disorder roared back at me louder than before and with even greater ferocity. From the moment I was admitted into the EDU, my E.D. was already fuming and furious like a raging wildfire, willing to destruct anything in its path in order to preserve itself. Because it was losing power so quickly, my E.D. cast even greater surges of anger down to those around me when I was first in treatment. This was especially true when it came to my family members who had loved and supported me ceaselessly throughout my struggles.

However, despite my disorder's fear of being defeated and its effort to fight against recovery, the EDU continued to push onward and attack with relentless rigidity. The counselors, therapists, and nurses at the EDU saw something in me that I could not see myself- a beam of light that shining past darkness; an inner strength breaking through a malnourished body; a whisper of hope competing against the terrifying thoughts anorexia was screaming.

And although not the case at first, eventually light, strength, and hope did begin to rise above my disease, and I did get better. Yet recovery was not a result that occurred overnight; it wasn't a simple act of simply swallowing a pill that would bring fast-acting relief, nor was did it involve dragging the issue out in the dirt and praying for a miracle to occur. It was an arduous and painful process that could only be accomplished by getting down on my hands and knees to dig out the root of the problem itself.

With the help of my family, friends, and treatment team, I built up a sturdy system of support that not even my eating disorder could sneak past. I replaced unhealthy food and exercise behaviors with positive coping mechanisms I was taught to use in the face of stressful situations.

I learned how to fight negative body image, as well as food restriction and exercise urges, with positive affirmations and other effective coping methods. I retaught myself how to eat in a proper way that did not involve disordered eating habits with the aid of my counselors and parents. I discovered new interests to provided myself with healthy emotional outlets, including painting, deep breathing, practicing yoga, and doing guided meditation and imagery with my mom. I developed a positive relationship with food by exposing myself to "fear foods" in the EDU, which were foods that my eating disorder had once forbidden me to eat because it had deemed them as being "unhealthy." I adapted my lifestyle to be once again involved in social experiences I had denied myself for so long, such as spending time with friends, eating at restaurants, and going to parties or sleepovers. I found love and respect for my body by first using radical acceptance to come to terms with the weight I had gained and then by eventually learning ways to celebrate my body and its amazing abilities. I saw the preciousness of life and how easily it can be taken from us through the hollow eyes of an E.D., the eyes of patients entering the EDU program just as I was leaving it. I shared my experience with as many trustworthy people I could in order to secure a safety net of support around me. I regained trust with my parents by showing that I was capable of being responsibility for my health by planning my own meals and maintaining my weight. I have made multiple visits to the EDU and reached out to people presently struggling with eating disorders. I have reflected on the progress I've made and opened my eyes to the abysmal trap of an E.D. that I never want to fall back into. I have allowed myself to let recovery into my body, mind, and soul in its purest and rawest form, which has proven to be both a horrific and beautiful thing. The scars of living with anorexia have since faded from my skin, but they will always lie deep within me as a reminder to myself that a dark past can never be fully erased, only painted over with the vibrant colors of a rediscovered life.

It brings unbelievable sadness to my heart to know that at this moment, there are millions of men and women across the world who are living with this deadly illness. To all of those people who are a part of that vast number, I tell you this: I am an eating disorder survivor. I empathize with your darkness and pain, and I know how it feels as you stand on the edge of recovery, with the idea seeming too impossible or too pointless or too terrifying to even take that first leap. For all of you, it is my responsibility as a survivor to tell you to keep fighting this battle. No matter how horrifying or difficult it is to face, recovery is possible and worth it. We who have struggled with darkness can discover our beacons of light and limitless potential. There is no greater gift in this world than finding the extraordinary life that exists beyond the barriers of an eating disorder.

3. The Story of My Eating Disorder

It's hard to pinpoint when and where my eating disorder started. Its development seemed to progress slowly through years of predisposing characteristics and experiences and then suddenly grow exponentially, hit a flipping point, and careen out of control. By the time I broke through my wall of denial, realizing I had anorexia nervosa, I felt that I was riding a wild horse of my creation, holding onto its mane for dear life with no say as to where we were going.

I was a happy child who grew up in a loving family. I loved to read, learn, organize, create, and wonder. I was close to my siblings and parents, especially my mother. From the beginning I was a perfectionist, I always wanted to do things as well as possible and as I grew older I wanted to reach my fullest potential in everything I did. As a homeschooler I did not have many peers to whom I could compare myself and therefore I competed with whatever ideal "best" self I could conceive. I always got As in school even once I began attending community college during my high school years. I excelled at playing the piano and spent hours practicing diligently. More and more I filled my life with expectations that were increasingly unattainable. If I reached a certain goal I simply popped up my expectations a notch like a reverse limbo-bar, barely allowing myself a moment of satisfaction. I had friends but often felt different, isolated, and alone. Yet, strangely, I was a leader around those I knew well. I was happy but I believe that this way of living provided fertile fields upon which my eating disorder later fed.

I really did not pay attention to body shape, weight, exercise, or eating until my teenage years. As a child I stubbornly opposed conforming to norms and cultural ideas. However, when puberty hit I noticed that my stomach was a bit rounder and when my father took me running and I could barely run a mile I labeled myself as out-of-shape. I started to think about what types of foods I ate. Beyond my 8-year-old conversion to vegetarianism I had never labeled foods as good or bad. Slowly I started to exercise more and eat more salads. I wanted to be healthy. And I was.

Then, the summer before my last year of high school, I went to Spain. While deeply immersed in the culture as my private Spanish teacher showed me her home city of Sevilla, I lost weight. Walking everywhere we went for hours a day and eating healthy as well as going on runs along the river to find some time alone caused me to unintentionally lose weight. I remember the moment I realized it; standing in the steamy bathroom of the 12th floor apartment I could see my ribs as I turned in the mirror and my skirt slipped off my hipbones. I did not know it at the time, but that is when the switch flipped. From there a cycle of "just-wanting-to-maintain-weight-but-still-losing-weight" began. I always told myself that I did not want to lose weight but because I was terrified of gaining weight I ran extra in the hot Spanish sun and ate less and less. The excuses of "not liking" certain foods and "not being hungry" began. When I returned home my mother was surprised by my change in weight but I assured her I was just being healthy. I lied to others and I lied to myself.

Over that next year the eating disorder grew and grew. I had already begun training to run a half marathon with my brother and father in the fall but now I ran the longer and longer distances with the motivation to burn calories. I ate less and less; I always made sure to eat something (because I told myself that way I couldn't have an eating disorder) but I began to restrict entire food groups and count calories. I weighed myself weekly and events in my life during that time are stamped with the numbers off the scale. I kept recipe books by my bed to dream of foods I would not eat. My period stopped. I ran more and more. I felt faint standing up too long. I fought with my mother about not eating enough. I was constantly cold and fearful. However, I convinced myself I was fine even as I became more and more miserable. On the outside I was a gorgeously smiling accomplished girl getting ready to head off to college—my siblings called me "perfect"—while on the inside I felt hollow and unfeeling.

In the spring of that year the denial finally shattered. After a couple conversations with my mother about how little I cared about *everything* in my life and how I constantly worried…no, not about school or college or anything she might expect, but about my weight and eating, I suddenly realized I had a problem. I hated admitting to the ugly inner thoughts that had come to direct my behaviors. I hated the voice in my head telling me I was not worthy. I hated…myself. The self-loathing paired with deep ambivalence toward everything I had once loved scared me enough to try therapy. Once I started reading books on eating disorders from the library and found I could check almost every symptom on the list for *anorexia nervosa*, I admitted I had a serious problem. As soon as I owned the fact that I had an eating disorder my perfectionist self kicked in from a new direction and I was determined to get better.

Recovery was not easy. I was exhausted by the constant vigilance necessary to combat the thoughts in my head that fought with meal plans, reduced exercise, no scales, and the positivity of therapy sessions. I felt that I could not win; I hated myself with the disorder and I hated myself in recovery. I suddenly realized what I had done to myself. I was angry, which suddenly showed me that I had numbed my emotions for a long while. I could not feel. All negative emotions were out of the question and positive feelings were tainted by guilt. I did not know what it meant to be hungry or full. My concentration was wrecked. I felt disgustingly fat even though I knew I was close to killing myself through weight loss. Nonetheless, I wanted recovery. I told myself that forcing myself to eat, going through the confusion of rediscovering feelings of pain and disgust and hatred, and going to therapy and nutrition sessions were all part of my punishment for failing at being perfect. I thought I deserved to suffer through recovery. But another part of me pushed to recover because I knew I deserved to live.

I was lucky to recover without relapse. I was in weekly therapy over the summer before college and through my freshman year of college. I worked hard and recovered quickly. Being able to focus my perfectionist energy on academics helped me immensely (although I then had to let go of that extreme focus as well). I found a support group in my new hometown. I became more comfortable talking about my struggle. I was able to spend the following summer back home without therapy and from there my sessions became less frequent. Over four years of college I learned to put energy into my true values instead of fill my life with eating disorder behaviors. I began to give back through mentoring, volunteering, speaking at events, and talking about my experience openly. Showing others recovery was possible motivated me to stay in recovery long term.

Five years later I consider myself entirely recovered and constantly in recovery. I believe I will always think differently about food, exercise, and my body. I will always have bad days when stress or triggers bring on the ugly voices. I will have seasons when I feel great and seasons when I dip into the struggle. I will always have the potential to grow in trusting myself and loving myself. However, being always in recovery does not mean I am not recovered. I entirely believe I am recovered. Yes, I still have bad days but over all I love my body, I love myself, and I love my life. I have worked hard to get to where I am and I still have a long way go but I am so grateful for what experiencing an eating disorder has taught me. It has made me who I am. I know I am one of the lucky ones and I would not wish an eating disorder on anyone, EVER, but I would not change my struggle with and recovery from anorexia for anything. I now know what it means to be whole.

4. Food is a Wonderful Thing (?)

Food is a wonderful thing, or is it? When college was stressful I thought one day I should start running, that would reduce stress and make me fit like so many others; and of course better looking. Forcing myself to run just added stress to my days, though. I am not a natural runner. In the mornings I rushed out of the house to get to school, usually without breakfast, but having coffee of course. Food can be expensive so I did not eat much during the day – but at night then I had the "big meal". After being stuffed I felt so uncomfortable that I felt I had to run, no matter whether it was 8PM or 12AM. This was my normal rhythm for a while. However, I noticed that I did not only gain (!) weight, but I also felt just uncomfortable all the time with how I looked and in which clothes size I fit in. It seemed only logical that I should not eat during the day, and the large meal at night, which was usually a multiple of a normal single portion, seemed just what I needed, but I also needed to "run it off". What I did not understand at the time was that I needed to not care about how big I felt, accept me as a worthy person no matter what size or weight, and THEN work on a healthy way of eating and exercising – to get out of this routine. Stress is a real killer though. It messes up everything. Learning to accept that I am not perfect although I always wanted to be, learning to see and accept that I am just like everyone else in so many ways was the road to feeling better and not use food to manage stress and feelings of emptiness when everything seemed to get too much.

Food can be a wonderful thing, but it can be abused as almost anything else to control how you feel. Don't be afraid of your feelings!

5. Isabelle's Slam Poem

All I can see is the way my stomach isn't flat, how my pelvis doesn't stick out to the point where it's shredding my skin, how my face is gaunt and looks like the prison I hold my body, my mind, in.

And there are women who are not young and in constant denial of themselves, women who have seen years and years and still refuse to feed themselves because all that matters is looking to as the men see fitting.

And there are women who want to punch the mirror but they won't because they think their husbands will only be mad about the glass on the floor, not about the glass in their hearts and in their skin. Even the people I know, people who support my journey through the struggle of eating and not eating secretly look in the mirror and think, "I'm fat."

And maybe there's a world where people look at you and think that you're pretty, but in this world, it's all about staying model-thin and making sure you eat nothing more than an apple. Even in my nurse's office, they say that a 1,000 calorie hamburger is going to ruin your life, that you should be cool, calm, and empty.

They say that people should be full of life, full of personality, but how can you be full in your heart when your stomach is empty, how can you be yourself when everyone is trying to be the model they're not.

When I was a little girl I wanted to be a model because I thought models were so lucky to be looked upon like Princesses and Queens. But I soon realized that their lives were filled with shots of tequila and coffee and wisps of cigarette smoke because those things supposedly lower your appetite. And all people think, write, speak about is child obesity, but they don't know that the people with the real problems with food are the girls and boys who throw up until their teeth turn the color of bile, until their throats scream in the agony of a thousand torn soldiers.

And however much I want it to change, people are constantly thinking and feeling about their body, how they're not good enough, how're they're fat...

And why can't they change?

They can't change because we've been warped into valuing the wrong things. You can't change people's minds, but you can change the coming generation. You can talk to your children, talk to them about how the loveliest people are not the perfect, fake ones, but the ones that are true and can live with themselves. There's more we can do with our lives than just selfishly think about ourselves, our bodies. We could be solving problems if we could just. Stop. Judging.

6. Episodes of a Journey

It is the beginning of April, 2015 and I am 12 years old and could not be happier. For the past month, I have been running after lacrosse every day, training for the Moab Half Marathon. At first I started gradually, and then the more I ran the more I became motivated to run. During my training for the half marathon, I also started lowering my food intake small bits at a time because of course I thought it would make me stronger and faster. At the Moab Half Marathon, I placed second in my age group and the girl who beat me was very tiny so it motivated me to get even smaller. Now, it is April and every day I want to exercise more and eat less food and the more weight I lose the more motivated I am to exercise more and restrict more. I am so excited because this gives me a great sense of control in my life and is a way I can help deal with stress. For as long as I can remember I have been a perfectionist, always wanting to do better in sports, get better grades and basically be perfect at everything. I have always been very active, but restricting my food intake and excessively exercising is a step closer for me to becoming perfect, so this is yet another reason why I am so thrilled. The only downside is my parents are making me see a therapist and a nutritionist every week because they are worried about me and believe that my excessive exercising and restrictive habits are not healthy. This makes me very angry because they just don't get that I am becoming so much stronger and healthier than I used to be. I am going in an upward spiral when they think I'm going down.

Now it is the end of August and I just got back from a canoe trip on the Green River that was a great trip, but there were times I was crying and very emotional over food. My family went with a few other families including my best friend's family and we spent a week on the river camping every night. During this trip, I isolated myself from everyone and just focused on getting enough exercise and restricting my food intake. While others were relaxing and interacting with each other, I was aggressively paddling up and down the river so I could get the exercise I needed. This was my number one priority and what I thought was fun. Now I am back to my home and am told I can't exercise for the time being. This makes me so frustrated because my parents don't realize how strong and lean I am getting. I look in the mirror and to me I see an overweight girl, but my parents keep telling me I am too lean. A couple days later we drive down to Children's Hospital for an evaluation at the Eating Disorder Unit. I sit in the waiting room while my parents are talking to one of the therapists, thinking to myself this is so silly and there is no way I will be admitted because nothing is wrong with me. After they are done talking, they invite me in to tell me that I will be admitted into the EDU that same day as an Extended Day Outpatient. I start hysterically crying because I am so confused and angry at my parents for bringing me here in the first place. Why are my parents making me give up on all my hard work?

I am currently in my last week of treatment at the EDU after being here for almost 7 weeks. School started a week after I got admitted and all that my peers know is that I have missed school due to a medical issue. Throughout my time here at the EDU I have had many ups and downs and am still working very hard to recover. I have realized that I do have a disease and most of the time realize that it is not making me stronger and healthier, but that it is making me much weaker and could even be fatal. There has also been many times that I have thought that the eating disorder is just getting worse and I will never recover, but have kept working hard with all my skills I have learned in the EDU and working with a therapist. During my first week at the EDU it was very hard for me to talk about my Eating Disorder because I believed that I still didn't have one and everyone around me was crazy. As my time at the EDU passed, I realized that I actually did have a disease and participating in therapy and groups would actually help me. One group that made a huge difference in my recovery was the creative arts therapy program because I could express my emotions through art and writing if they were too hard to talk about. The support of the other patients and families was a major part of my recovery as well as my own family and my hospital care team. There were countless times where I would feel even worse after therapy because it was so emotional, but looking back on it I would still be where I was when I was admitted 7 weeks ago if I had not been open during therapy. Now I am leaving the EDU and I am excited, but also scared because I have been in this safe sanctuary for the past 7 weeks and have not been exposed to the outside world.

Almost one year from when I was admitted, I am now proud to say that I do not obsess about food 24 hours a day although eating is still hard for me and I still have challenge foods. I eat very healthy but do not believe that restricting my eating and over exercising will make me healthier. Many people have asked me what has changed since I was first admitted to the EDU and I believe that what helped the most is not giving up, being open in therapy, challenging the eating disorder, the support from my parents and thinking about my important values and my true goals in life. It is now much easier for me to separate my eating disorder from myself and think of all my better values that are more important to me. Some of my most important values are going to college, being strong and healthy, becoming a neurosurgeon one day, and having a healthy relationship with my family, which could not be accomplished with an eating disorder in my life. Eating disorders are very complicated, but I am working very hard everyday to get closer to a full recovery and the most important thing that I think I have learned is that there is no easy fix to recovering from eating disorders, but that it is a process that is different for everyone.

15. References and Further Reading

1. Dignon A, Beardsmore A, Spain S, Kuan A. 'Why I won't eat': patient testimony from 15 anorexics concerning the causes of their disorder. J Health Psychol. 2006;11(6):942-56.

2. Crow SJ, Peterson CB, Swanson SA, Raymond NC, Specker S, Eckert ED, et al. Increased mortality in bulimia nervosa and other eating disorders. Am J Psychiatry. 2009;166(12):1342-6.

3. Arcelus J, Mitchell AJ, Wales J, Nielsen S. Mortality rates in patients with anorexia nervosa and other eating disorders. A meta-analysis of 36 studies. Arch Gen Psychiatry. 2011;68(7):724-31.

4. Hudson JI, Hiripi E, Pope HG, Jr., Kessler RC. The prevalence and correlates of eating disorders in the National Comorbidity Survey Replication. Biol Psychiatry. 2007;61(3):348-58.

5. Special Issue: Medical Issues in Eating Disorders. Int J Eat Disord. 32016. p. 205-344.

6. Engel GL. The biopsychosocial model and the education of health professionals. Ann N Y Acad Sci. 1978;310:169-87.

7. Allen M, Williams G. Consciousness, plasticity, and connectomics: the role of intersubjectivity in human cognition. Front Psychol. 2011;2:20.

8. De Ridder D, Elgoyhen AB, Romo R, Langguth B. Phantom percepts: tinnitus and pain as persisting aversive memory networks. Proc Natl Acad Sci U S A. 2011;108(20):8075-80.

9. Frank GK. The Perfect Storm - A Bio-Psycho-Social Risk Model for Developing and Maintaining Eating Disorders. Front Behav Neurosci. 2016;10:44.
10. Fichter MM, Quadflieg N. Mortality in eating disorders - results of a large prospective clinical longitudinal study. Int J Eat Disord. 2016;49(4):391-401.
11. Olmsted MP, Kaplan AS, Rockert W. Relative efficacy of a 4-day versus a 5-day day hospital program. Int J Eat Disord. 2003;34(4):441-9.
12. Lock J, La Via MC, American Academy of C, Adolescent Psychiatry Committee on Quality I. Practice parameter for the assessment and treatment of children and adolescents with eating disorders. J Am Acad Child Adolesc Psychiatry. 2015;54(5):412-25.
13. Zeeck A, Weber S, Sandholz A, Wetzler-Burmeister E, Wirsching M, Hartmann A. Inpatient versus day clinic treatment for bulimia nervosa: a randomized trial. Psychother Psychosom. 2009;78(3):152-60.
14. Rigaud DJ, Brayer V, Roblot A, Brindisi MC, Verges B. Efficacy of tube feeding in binge-eating/vomiting patients: a 2-month randomized trial with 1-year follow-up. JPEN Journal of parenteral and enteral nutrition. 2011;35(3):356-64.
15. Frank GK. Could dopamine agonists aid in drug development for anorexia nervosa? Front Nutr. 2014;1:19.

16. Frank GK. Aripiprazole, a partial dopamine agonist to improve adolescent anorexia nervosa-A case series. Int J Eat Disord. 2016;49(5):529-33.
17. Frank G, Hagman J, Solomon M. Eating Disorders in Children and Adolescents. Colorado Journal of Psychiatry & Psychology. 2015;1(1):50-68.
18. Findlay S, Pinzon J, Taddeo D, Katzman D. Family-based treatment of children and adolescents with anorexia nervosa: Guidelines for the community physician. Paediatr Child Health. 2010;15(1):31-40.
19. Hildebrandt T, Bacow T, Markella M, Loeb KL. Anxiety in anorexia nervosa and its management using family-based treatment. European eating disorders review : the journal of the Eating Disorders Association. 2012;20(1):e1-16.
20. Lock J, Le Grange D, Agras WS, Moye A, Bryson SW, Jo B. Randomized clinical trial comparing family-based treatment with adolescent-focused individual therapy for adolescents with anorexia nervosa. Arch Gen Psychiatry. 2010;67(10):1025-32.

Practice Guidelines

Practice Guideline for the Treatment of Patients With Eating Disorders, Third Edition
http://psychiatryonline.org/pb/assets/raw/sitewide/practice_guidelines/guidelines/eatingdisorders.pdf

Practice Parameter for the Assessment and Treatment
of Children and Adolescents with Eating
Disorders
https://www.aacap.org/App_Themes/AACAP/docs/prac
tice_parameters/Eating%20Disorders%20JAACA
P%20Submit%20final.pdf

Self Screening

Self Screening for Eating Disorders, Eating Attitudes
Test (EAT-26)
http://eat-26.com/Form/

Eating Disorder Organizations

Academy for Eating Disorders
www.aedweb.org

ABOUT-FACE!
www.about-face.org

Alliance for Eating Disorders Awareness
www.allianceforeatingdisorders.com

Andrea's Voice Foundation
www.andreasvoice.org

Binge Eating Disorder Association
www.bedaonline.com

The Body Positive
www.thebodypositive.org

Community Outreach for Prevention of Eating
Disorders
www.cope-ecf.org

Eating Disorders Anonymous
www.eatingdisordersanonymous.org

Eating Disorders Coalition for Research, Policy and
Action
www.eatingdisorderscoalition.org

Eating Disorder Hope
www.eatingdisorderhope.com

Eating Disorder Network of Central Florida
www.edncf.org

Eating Disorders Referral and Information
www.edreferral.com

Eating Disorders Coalition of Tennessee
www.edct.net

Eating Disorders Foundation
www.eatingdisorderfoundation.org

EDIN: Eating Disorders Information Network
www.myedin.org

EDN: Eating Disorder Network of Maryland
www.ednmaryland.org

Eating For Life Alliance
www.eatingforlife.org

The Elisa Project
www.theelisaproject.org

FEAST: Families Empowered and Supporting
Treatment of Eating Disorders
www.feast-ed.org

FREED Foundation
www.freedfoundation.org

H.O.P.E.: Helping Other People Eat
www.hopetolive.com

International Association of Eating Disorders
Professionals
www.iaedp.com
Joy Project
www.joyproject.org

The Kirsten Haglund Foundation
www.kirstenhaglund.org

Manna Scholarship Fund
www.mannafund.org

Maudsley Parents
www.maudselyparents.org

Mentor Connect
www.mentorconnect-ed.org

Missouri Eating Disorders Association
www.moeatingdisorders.org

National Association of Anorexia Nervosa &
Associated Disorders
www.anad.org

National Association For Males with Eating
Disorders
www.namedinc.org

National Eating Disorders Association
www.nationaleatingdisorders.org

National Eating Disorder Information Centre
www.nedic.ca

Normal in Schools
www.normal-life.org

Oklahoma Eating Disorders Association
www.okeatingdisorders.org

Project Heal
www.theprojectheal.org